KŪSHYĀR IBN LABBĀN

PRINCIPLES OF HINDU RECKONING

KŪSHYĀR IBN LABBĀN

PRINCIPLES OF HINDU RECKONING

A TRANSLATION
WITH INTRODUCTION AND NOTES BY
MARTIN LEVEY AND MARVIN PETRUCK
OF THE
KITĀB FĪ USŪL HISĀB AL-HIND

THE UNIVERSITY OF WISCONSIN PRESS
MADISON AND MILWAUKEE: 1965

PUBLISHED BY THE UNIVERSITY OF WISCONSIN PRESS
MADISON AND MILWAUKEE
P.O. BOX 1379, MADISON, WISCONSIN, 53701

PRINTED IN THE UNITED STATES OF AMERICA
LIBRARY OF CONGRESS CATALOG CARD NUMBER 65-12106

TO THE MEMORY OF

DR. JOSEF WEINBERG

A YOUNG HISTORIAN OF MATHEMATICS WHOSE WORK WAS CUT SHORT BY BULLETS AS HE WAS ESCAPING FROM A TRAIN TAKING HIM AND OTHERS TO A CONCENTRATION CAMP IN 1944

FOREWORD

The publication of Kūshyār ibn Labbān's *Principles of Hindu Reckoning* represents a new departure for Wisconsin's *Publications in Medieval Science*, the publication of Arabic scientific works of the medieval period. It is true that in my earlier volume, *Archimedes in the Middle Ages: The Arabo-Latin Tradition*, where the objective was to make-available and to analyze the medieval Latin works dependent on the Arabic tradition of Archimedes, one of the principal Arabic geometrical treatises, the *Verba filiorum* of the famous mathematicians, the Banū Mūsā, was published in its Latin translation. But in the volume at hand, it is an Arabic text itself that is under study. In this volume the editors have translated and discussed one of the most important of the Arabic arithmetical treatises. It may be "the oldest surviving mathematical text [in Arabic] using the Hindu numerals," as the editors remark. It has been the intention of the editors to point out in the introduction and the notes the elements of originality in the text, to show that the Arabs were more than mere transmitters of earlier science.

Before remarking briefly on the importance of Kūshyār's work, let me call the reader's attention to a succinct statement of the scope and objectives of arithmetic as given by al-Fārābī in his celebrated *Enumeration of the Sciences*, written no doubt some decades prior to Kūshyār's tract:[1]

As for arithmetic, there are two sciences which are known by this name: practical arithmetic and theoretical arithmetic. Practical arithmetic inquires into numbers insofar as the numbers are fixed to things numbered, i.e., bodies and other things whose enumeration it is necessary to have, like men, horses, dinars, dirhams, or other things possessed of number. This is the arithmetic that the people use in the commercial transactions of the market and the city. Theoretical arithmetic inquires into numbers in the abstract insofar as they are separated in the mind from bodies and everything else which is numbered by

[1] A. Gonzalez Palencia, *Alfarabi, Catalogo de las Ciencias* (Madrid, 1932), Arabic text, p. 33.

them. . . . And it is this latter arithmetic which investigates numbers in an independent manner (i.e., in the abstract) with regard to (1) everything which happens to them in their simple essences without mutually comparing them, for example: their being even or odd, and (2) everything which happens to them when they are mutually compared, for example: their being equal; or one being more than another (i.e., their being unequal); or one number being a part or parts of another number, or double it, or equal to it with the addition of a part or parts; or like numbers being proportional or not being proportional, similar or dissimilar, commensurable or incommensurable. Furthermore, theoretical arithmetic inquires into what happens to numbers upon addition and their resulting sum, their subtraction and resulting difference, their multiplication, and their division. This is like numbers being squared, or representing surfaces or solids, or being perfect or imperfect. Thus theoretical arithmetic investigates all of these things and whatever happens to numbers when they are mutually compared. It teaches how to find [unknown] numbers from known ones, and, in short, every way of finding numbers.

But Kūshyār's considerations are much more specific. The reader will observe that Kūshyār has divided his work into two main parts, the first of which treats the fundamental operations with integers in the decimal notation, while the second part centers on sexagesimal reckoning. The Arabic author's terse and abbreviated style makes the editors' translation and commentary in the notes particularly useful for the proper understanding of the work. The review of Arabic arithmetical terminology used by Kūshyār and other authors is especially welcome to the reader first venturing into a detailed consideration of Arabic arithmetic. The dust board procedures as summarized in the Introduction are also of considerable help to the reader when he turns to the text. Likewise helpful are the summaries of the procedures for sexagesimal reckoning which in the Introduction are placed beside the comparable operations with integers in the decimal system. The editors point out that "Kūshyār understood and demonstrated almost a pure sexagesimal procedure for all but the cube root operation," and in this he shows marked superiority over most other medieval arithmeticians.

With the publication of this work, the editors have produced an important contribution to the understanding of the rise and spread of Hindu reckoning. Using this volume as background, the reader will turn with greater perception to the medieval Latin arithmetics of the high and late Middle Ages.

MARSHALL CLAGETT
Institute for Advanced Study, Princeton

PREFACE

Kūshyār ibn Labbān's *Principles of Hindu Reckoning*, the subject of this work, is singularly important in the history of mathematics, not only for its mathematical content, but also for its linguistic interest and its relation to earlier and succeeding algorisms. It may be the oldest Arabic mathematical text using the Hindu numerals, and ibn Labbān's concepts reveal considerable originality. The authors hope by publishing this work to demonstrate that the Arabs were not only transmitters of other cultures, but made their own significant contributions as well.

In the translation we have maintained, as much as possible, a middle course between preserving the medieval flavor of the original and striving for clarity in the mathematical processes, for the benefit of modern readers. At all times we have attempted to bring into the technical context any literary quality inherent in the original work. Marginal additions in the manuscript are in a number of different hands other than that of the text itself, except in rare cases. They do not belong to the text itself as may be seen by checking the Hebrew version. These have been omitted in the translation. Where the hand is the same as in the text, the translation accounts for it or carries it over into English, depending on the particular context.

Our translation is based on the only extant manuscript of ibn Labbān's work in Arabic: Istanbul, Aya Sophya Library, MS 4857, (fols. 267b-282b), and a Hebrew translation and commentary by Shālôm ben Joseph ʿAnābī: Oxford, Bodleian Library, Oppenheim 211.

The Arabic text was microfilmed and reproduced by permission of the Government of the Turkish Republic and through the graciousness of the Director of the Suleymaniye Library of Istanbul, Mr. H. Dener, and his associates, who have always shown the utmost kindness toward the work of Arabic scholars. For a photostat copy of the Hebrew text we are indebted to the late Professor Solomon Gandz.

A National Institutes of Health research grant (RG 7391) to M.L. helped make work on this book possible. M. McG. L. carried out the task of reading, checking, and ordering this volume with the same understanding and finesse she has lavished on the previous works of M.L. We wish also to express our gratitude to Dr. Judith Sachs, Librarian of the Institute for Advanced Study, who showed thoughtfulness and consideration at all times, especially during the period when the book was being completed.

MARTIN LEVEY
MARVIN PETRUCK

July 15, 1963

CONTENTS

INTRODUCTION

INTRODUCTION

Kūshyār ibn Labbān and His Works

The apogee of Arabic science in the Middle East came during the tenth and eleventh centuries. Particularly in mathematics, this was an active and fruitful period that produced not only translations and commentaries on Greek and other sources, but many original works in the Arabic language.

Some of this original Arabic work is to be found in the algorismic development of the fundamental arithmetical operations. Before the tenth century, al-Khwārizmī was the first to write a work on this subject (*ca.* 820), but unfortunately the Arabic text has not survived, and his work is known only through a much later (twelfth-century) Latin translation. However, abū Kāmil Shujā', the "Egyptian Calculator," who lived shortly after al-Khwārizmī, elaborated on the latter's algebra.[1] Abū Kāmil's work greatly influenced the thirteenth-century mathematician Leonardo Fibonacci and through him later European mathematics.

In the tenth century a Persian, abū al-Wafā' (940-*ca.* 997), who was one of the last great translators and commentators on Euclid, Diophantos, and Ptolemy, wrote an Arabic work on arithmetic, *Kitāb fī mā yaḥtāj ilaihi al-kuttāb wa'l-ummāl min 'ilm al-ḥisāb*. He did not, however, use the Arabic (or Hindu, as the Arabs called them) numerals. The next algorismic work known (probably about 1000) was by Kūshyār ibn Labbān, the *Kitāb fī uṣūl ḥisāb al-hind* which is the subject of our study. This text, still extant in the original Arabic, is of particular interest because it is the oldest surviving Arabic work using Hindu numerals in the algorisms (it preceded al-Karajī's *Kāfī fī al-ḥisāb*, written in the early part of the eleventh century and also surviving in the Arabic). But it is significant also for its place in the development of mathematical terminology and concepts.

[1] A study by Martin Levey, of abū Kāmil's algebra, from the Arabic and Hebrew texts, is now in press (University of Wisconsin Press).

Kūshyār ibn Labbān (*fl. ca.* 971-*ca.* 1029) was primarily an astronomer. His home was in Jīlān, a village south of the Caspian Sea in Persia. The name of his father, Labbān or Labbār meant "lion,"[2] in the local Indo-European dialect, and Kūshyār[3] himself was variously cited as Kusyān, Kūshiyad, Kōshār, Kūsiar, and Kōssar. Other variants for his name were Jabah, Halebi, and al-Kiya.[4] It has been stated that ibn Labbān was a Jew, but the evidence is still inconclusive.[5] Very little of the biography of ibn Labbān has come down to us. The sole important fact known, aside from his works, is that he was the teacher of the well-known algorist, al-Nasawī (*fl. ca.* 1030). [6]

Several of Kūshyār's works have survived, particularly those on astronomy and geography,[7] his major interests. His astronomical tables, *Al-zīj al-jāmiʿ*, were cited by abū al-Fadāʿ (fourteenth century).[8] In addition, the Bibliothèque Nationale, Paris, possesses a treatise written by Kūshyār on the astrolabe, *Kitāb al-asṭurlāb wakaifīyat ʿamalihī waʿtibārihī ʿala al-tamām wal-kamāl.* Other works[9] are *Kitāb al-mudkhal fī ṣināʿat aḥkām al-nujūm*, and *Risala al-abʿād wal-ajrām.*

Finally, there is the mathematical work, *Kitāb fī uṣūl ḥisāb al-hind*,[10] presented here in our translation and extant in Arabic in only one manuscript.[11] There is also extant a Hebrew translation and commentary on the Arabic text, called *ʿĪyyūn hāʿiqqārīm*,[12] written by Shālôm ben Joseph ʿAnābī, who lived in Constantinople in the 15th Century. The

[2] Mohammad Shafiʿ, ed., *Abū al-Ḥasan ʿAlī ibn Funduq, Tatimma Ṣiwan al-Ḥikma* (Lahore, 1935), **1**, 83-84, Biog. 43.

[3] Moritz Steinschneider, *Die Hebraeischen Uebersetzungen des Mittelalters* (Berlin, 1893); see also Steinschneider, *Zeitschrift der Deutschen Morgenländischen Gesellschaft*, **24**, 375 (1860-62).

[4] *Lexicon bibliographicum et encyclopaedicum a Mustapha ben Abdallah Katib Jele bi dicto et nomine Haji Khalfa celebrato compositum, latine vertit et commentario indicibusque instruxit*, Gustav Flügel (Leipzig, London, 1835), **5**, 82, 142; **7**, 851.

[5] Johannes Tropfke, *Geschichte der Elementar-Mathematik* (Berlin, 1930), **1**, 82; Paul Luckey, *Die Rechenkunst bei Ǧamšīd b. Masʿūd al-Kāšī* (Wiesbaden, 1951), p. 73.

[6] See Heinrich Suter, *Bibliotheca Mathematica*, Ser. III, **7**, 113-19 (1906); Franz Woepcke, *Journal Asiatique*, **1**, 492-500 (1863).

[7] Joachim Lelewel, *Géographie du Moyen Age* (Brussels, 1852), **1**, xlviii.

[8] Joseph Toussaint Reinaud and William MacGuckin de Slane, eds., *Géographie d'Aboulféda* (Paris, 1840), **1**, ci. For these tables, see E. S. Kennedy, "A Survey of Islamic Astronomical Tables," *Transactions of the American Philosophical Society*, N.S. **46**, pt. 2 (1956).

[9] Carl Brockelmann, *Geschichte der Arabischen Literatur* (Leiden, 1943), **1**, 222; Suppl., **1**, 397.

[10] The *Maqala al-ūlā fī ḥisāb al-abwāb min al-maqalat al-arbaʿ*, is listed by Brockelmann erroneously as being another copy of this book. Actually it is a copy of his *zīj*.

[11] MS Istanbul, Aya Sofya Library, 4857 (fols. 267b-282b); see M. Krause, "Stambuler Handschriften Islamischer Mathematiker," *Quellen und Studien zur Geschichte der Mathematik, Astronomie und Physik*, **3**, 472-73 (1936).

[12] MS Oxford, Bodleian Library, Oppenheim 211; *see* Steinschneider, *Zeitschrift für Mathematik und Physik*, **12**, 33 (1867).

commentary was completed sometime between 1450 and 1460.[13] We have used both the Arabic text and the Hebrew commentary in our study.

The Arabic text is divided into two books. The first is concerned mainly with the decimal system for integers and fundamental operations without recourse to the sexagesimal tables; the second book takes up pure sexagesimal reckoning using these tables in a somewhat limited manner we shall describe later. The Hebrew commentary, however, covers only the material of Book I and comprises the following twelve chapters: numeration, addition and doubling, subtraction and halving, multiplication, results of multiplication, division, results of division, square root, results of square root, cube root, results of cube root, and checking by casting out nines. The sections on "results" describe the powers of the preceding solutions. The first eight chapters correspond to the first eight of the Arabic Book I. The twelfth Hebrew chapter is a commentary on the last Arabic chapter of Book I. In chapter 9 the commentary discusses the results of square root and in chapters 10 and 11 deals with the cube root, which is not taken up until Book II, chapter 16, of the Arabic. The commentary is, throughout, very detailed and in fact considers some other points of the sexagesimal system, so that in it not all of the Arabic Book II is missing. In this way the commentator attempted to cover the two books of ibn Labbān's work in a summary fashion.

Ibn Labbān's Arabic text was written in a highly abbreviated style that must have been difficult to understand when studied alone. It is easily seen, therefore, why al-Nasawī found it worthwhile to elaborate on the work of his teacher, and why ʿAnābī wrote his commentary. The interesting point is that Kūshyār's text was still widely enough used in the fifteenth century to warrant a commentary.

As to the Arabic text translated into Hebrew by ʿAnābī, it was certainly not the one now known in the Aya Sofya Library. Some of the quotations found in the Hebrew text are not to be found in the unique Arabic manuscript. In addition, some of the problems are different. There must have been many texts of Kūshyār ibn Labbān's arithmetic at one time, but with the change from use of the dust board to a more permanent form of writing, the technique for algorisms changed, and the earlier texts probably lost much of their usefulness. The dust board was a writing surface on which sand or wax was spread and was, like a blackboard, convenient for making running calculations. It induced, however, the erasing and altering of figures at each step of the operation, leading to a "dust board" technique of reckoning quite distinct from the method

[13] Steinschneider, *Heb. Uebersetz.*, p. 124; Johann Christoph Wolf, *Bibliotheca Hebraea* (Hamburg, 1715-33); Steinschneider, *Hebraeischen Bibliographie* (Berlin, 1858-64), **16**, 103.

employed when each step is retained in writing (*takht*, "dust board," "dust surface").

Numeration

The Sumerians were the earliest to develop a complete system of sexagesimal calculation which included both integers and fractions, but it is uncertain precisely how this mathematical system was transmitted eventually to the writers in Arabic. It is known, however, that Ptolemy and Theon used sexagesimal fractions although they used a decimal notation for integers. In India, the Bakhshālī manuscript (200 A.D.), Āryabhaṭa (499 A.D.), Bhāskara I (522 A.D.), Lalla (598 A.D.), and Brahmagupta (628 A.D.) used the place-value notation for decimal integers, and the system may have been known earlier.

The Hindu numerals were known to the early Arabic mathematicians. Many references to these and to Hindu mathematics in general are to be found in the works of the Muslims. The Syrian ibn Waḥshīya (middle of the ninth century)[14] was one of the early Muslim authors to mention the Hindu numerals as an alphabet. But evidence that the numerals were probably known to other Syrians early in the seventh century is found in the writings of Severus Sabokt,[15] bishop of a monastery on the Euphrates near Diarbekr, who was much interested in Hindu mathematics.

Al-Jāḥiẓ (d. 868-869),[16] the philosopher, and al-Mas'ūdī[17] (d. 956) both attribute the origin of these numerals to the Hindus. Abū Sahl ibn Tamim (d. 950)[18] wrote in the *Sefer Yezirah* that he had used the nine signs in his work on Hindu calculation, *Ḥisāb al-ghubāṛ*. Al-Nadīm (d. 995), in the *Fihrist*, mentioned the Hindu numerals.[19]

Ibn Labbān, in his opening sentence, describes his book as one on the principles of Hindu arithmetic and gives the nine numerals (reading from the right) as follows: ٩٨٧٦٥٤٣٢١. He used a circle as a zero.

Al-Karajī,[20] in the early eleventh century, wrote of nine symbols and

[14] *Ancient alphabets and hieroglyphic characters explained, etc.* Text and translation by Joseph Hammer-Purgstall (London, 1806).

[15] F. Naŭ, "La plus ancienne mention orientale des chiffres indiens," *Journal asiatique*, **16**, 225-27 (1910).

[16] B. Carra de Vaux, *Scientia*, **21**, 273-82 (1921).

[17] Joseph Toussaint Reinaud, *Mémoire sur l'Inde* (Paris, 1894), p. 300.

[18] *Ibid.*, p. 399.

[19] *Kitāb al-fihrist*, ed., Flügel (Leipzig, 1871-72), **2**, 18-19.

[20] Adolf Hochheim, transl., *Kāfī fīl Hisāb des Abū Bekr Alhusein Alkarkhi* (Magdeburg, 1878-79), **1**, 4.

three orders, as did al-Ḥaṣṣār (twelfth century)[21] and ibn al-Bannā' (first half of the thirteenth century).[22] The Hindus gave names to the orders, some of them up to twenty-four, as in Mahāvīrācārya.[23]

In Latin works, partly under the influence of the abacists, there were usually three orders named: units, tens, and hundreds. A very popular work of Sacrobosco (thirteenth century) relates:

Numerus quidem dupliciter notificatur, formaliter et materialiter: formaliter ut numerus est multitudo ex unitatibus aggregata: materialiter ut numerus est unitates collectae. Unitas autem est qua unaquaeque res una dicitur. Numerorum alius digitus; alius articulus; alius numerus compositus sive mixtus. Digitus quidem dicitus omnis numerus qui potest dividi in decem partes aequales, ita quod nihil residuum sit; compositus vero sive mixtus est qui constat ex digito et articulo.[24]

Savasorda, who introduced decimal integral calculation to Europe in the early twelfth century, used an indicator, a mark above the numeral, to denote its order. This was necessary in his case, since he did not use a zero in his text. Savasorda's was the first description in medieval Europe of an indicator symbol in an algorism. It is clear from his account that the system was derived from an Arabic treatise. Much earlier, however, the Egyptians[25] had used indicators to denote the orders up to one million. These hieroglyphs ascended in the orders of ten. The Babylonians, using the sexagesimal system, had less need for symbols to indicate orders than did those using the decimal system. The much greater difference in value between two succeeding orders in the sexagesimal than in the decimal system made an error in the former system much more obvious. Later on, however, the Babylonians did invent a zero.[26]

Kūshyār ibn Labbān, although much earlier than Savasorda, knew of the zero and used it throughout his work, thus precluding much of the

[21] Suter, ed., "Das Rechenbuch des Abu Zakaraja el-Hassar," *Bibl. Math.* Ser. III, **2**, 12-40 (1901).

[22] Suzan Rose Benedict, *A Comparative Study of the Early Treatises Introducing into Europe the Hindu Art of Reckoning* (Concord, N.H., 1916), p. 37.

[23] *Ibid.*, p. 33.

[24] J. O. Halliwell[-Phillipps], ed., *Rara Mathematica* (London, 1839), contains *Tractatus de Arte Numerandi* by Johannis de Sacro-Bosco, p. 2.

[25] K. Sethe, "Von Zahlen und Zahlworten bei den alten Aegyptern," *Schriften der Wissenschaftlichen Gesellschaft*, **25** (Strassbourg, 1916); Alan Henderson Gardiner, *Egyptian Grammar* (London, 1950), Par. 259; Otto Neugebauer, *Vorlesungen über Geschichte der antiken mathematischen Wissenschaften* (Berlin, 1934).

[26] Otto Neugebauer, *The Exact Sciences in Antiquity* (Providence, 1957), p. 28. Although the zero was in full use from 300 B.C. on, the earliest use of the "zero" dates back much earlier. Samuel Langdon tentatively dated a table of squares to the period of Darius (Kish 500 B.C.); this table contains four cases of a "zero" as in 30. The "zero" is omitted in one case. There is also the possibility of an earlier date (about 700 B.C.). See Neugebauer and Abraham Sachs, *Mathematical Cuneiform Texts* (New Haven, 1945), p. 34, note 95.

necessity for an order indicator. He not only omitted any sign indicating place position, he also avoided any symbol to separate a fraction from the integral part of a number. It was not until the twelfth century that Abraham ben Meir ibn Ezra[27] used a very effective symbol, a vertical line, to separate the integral from the fractional elements. This separator notation was well known to such later Jewish mathematicians as Levi ben Gerson (d. 1344) and Mordecai Comtino (d. 1482), who used it for sexagesimals, and to Elijah ben Abraham Mizrachi (d. *ca.* 1525),[28] whose notation exerted a great influence upon the developing arithmetic of the West. Simon Stevin (d. 1620) used a clumsy notation in which the number (i.e. of a particular order) is followed by its order designation enclosed in a circle.[29]

The numerals used in the Hebrew text are, except for the five, the same as those found in the Arabic treatise. Frequently, throughout their more rhetorical sections, the two texts use letters, Arabic or Hebrew, instead of the Hindu notation. Their values are based on the alphabetic arrangement of one of the very old Semitic languages, and the practice is usually referred to as the abjad or abgad system, after the arrangement of the first three letters, in Hebrew a, b, g, and correspondingly in Arabic and Greek. These letters are so commonly in use today, as well as in the manuscripts, that they bear repetition.

	1	2	3	4	5	6	7	8	9	10	20	30	40	50
	a	b	g	d	h	w	z	ḥ	ṭ	i	k	l	m	n
ʿAnābī	א	ב	ג	ד	ה	ו	ז	ח	ט	י	כ	ל	ם	נ
Kūshyār	ا	ب	ج	د	ه	و	ز	ح	ط	ي	ك	ل	م / ـمـ	ن / ـنـ
Greek	α	β	γ	δ	ϵ	ς	ζ	η	θ	ι	κ	λ	μ	ν

[27] Moritz Silberberg, ed., *Sefer ha-Mispar by Abraham ibn Ezra* (Frankfurt am Main, 1895); G. Sarton, *Isis*, **23**, 226, fig. 46 (1935).

[28] Sarton, *Isis*, **23**, 173.

[29] Simon Stevin, *Pratique d'arithmétique* (Leiden, 1585); Sarton, *Isis*, **23**, 230-44.

MATHEMATICAL TERMINOLOGY

Before we proceed to a description of the fundamental operations found in Kūshyār ibn Labbān's work on arithmetic, it will be useful to discuss his mathematical terms in some detail. For students of scientific terminology, ibn Labbān's work has a distinct interest, since it may be the earliest arithmetical text surviving in Arabic. The terminology is relatively unsophisticated, compared with that found in such later writers as al-Kāshī and al-Qalaṣādī in the fifteenth century. A number of Kūshyār's usages are the earliest found in Arabic; he adapted many common expressions to give them special mathematical meanings. The etymology of his terms is therefore revealing of the development of Muslim mathematical thought during his period. While Kūshyār was able, by evolving his own terms, to convey many subtleties, he was at the same time hampered by insufficient understanding, particularly in the area of exponents, and therefore failed to develop the discrete terminology which would have enabled him to make an advanced synthesis. This will be evident when we discuss the particular expressions he used.

The simpler terms deserve a quick summary: First, the symbols for the numerals are called *ṣuwar al-ḥurūf*. The term for the place order, when written as a number, is *rutba*, from *rattaba*, "to arrange," to "stand in order." When a number is decimal, there are the terms: *āḥād*, for the order of the "units"; *asharāt*, for the order of the "tens"; *mā'īn*,[30] for "hundreds"; *ulūf*, for "thousands"; *asharāt ulūf*, for "ten thousands"; *mā'īn ulūf*, for "hundred thousands," and so on to hundred thousand thousands. The rank of an order is referred to as *marātib*. The zero is *ṣifr*.

In the process of addition, *ziyāda*, ibn Labbān uses no specialized terms for addend or augend, nor does he have names in subtraction, *nuqṣān*, for minuend or subtrahend, though these exist in later Arabic and Hebrew. "To subtract" or "to cast out" is *alaqa*. A form of subtraction is *tanṣīf*, or "halving," from the verb *naṣafa*, "to halve."

In multiplication, the "lower number," *suflānīya*, is the multiplier, and the "upper number," *fauqāniya*, is the multiplicand. The "product" is *ḥāṣil min al-ḍarb*, or "result of multiplication." "To double" is *ḍā'afa*. Another word for "multiplier" is *maḍrūb fīhī* or just *maḍrūb*. The product, especially in sexagesimal operations is often called *mablagh* (pl: *mabāligh*).

In division, *qisma*, ibn Labbān has "divisor" as *maqsūm 'alaihu*, and "dividend" as *maqsūm*. The "quotient" or "result of division" is *ḥāṣil min al-qisma*. "Remainder" is *bāqī*.

[30] Unusual spelling. See Arabic glossary.

The "square root" is *jadhr*, and "cube root" *kaʿb*. These are both very old terms. The former has many connotations in earlier work.

"Shift" is *naqala* in the above operations and in the checking operation the "check" or "indicator" is *mīzān*.

In Book II, where ibn Labbān discusses the sexagesimal system together with operations pertaining to it, many highly technical terms appear. In this system (later called *al-arqām al-sittīnīya* by al-Kāshī), Kūshyār refers to the units as *daraja*. The lower orders are, respectively: "minutes," *daqāʾiq*; "seconds," *thawānī*; "thirds," *thawālith*; "fourths," *rawābiʿ*; and so on. For powers higher than the degree he uses a quite different system of names. The second power is designated as "twice raised," *marfūʿ marratain*i, and the fourth is "raised four times," *marfūʿ arbaʿ marrāt*.

The word "raised" probably entered Arabic mathematics about the time of ibn Labbān. It is used in a sense contrary to that of *basṭ*, a process of "spreading" in which all the higher orders of a sexagesimal number are multiplied by their respective powers of sixty, starting with the highest, to reduce them to the units of the lowest. "Raising" consists in dividing through by sixty at a time to obtain the various orders of the sexagesimal amount. The actual word "raised," *marfūʿ* (*mūrām* in Hebrew), is a very simple term, but Kūshyār uses it to indicate, after a fashion, the power of the sexagesimal order.

Al-Nasawī employed the process of *basṭ*, which essentially converts a sexagesimal to a decimal number by bringing the sexagesimal to the "type of the last fraction," *jins al-kasr al-akhīr*. Many mathematicians used this process of conversion to avoid more difficult sexagesimal operations.

Sibṭ al-Maradīnī, the sixteenth-century mathematician and astronomer, improved and clarified ibn Labbān's system by denoting not only "raised" (*al-marfūʿāt*) but also "lowered" (*al-maḥṭuṭāt*) numbers. When Sibṭ refers to lower orders, he says, "on the side of the lower," *fī jānib al-ḥaṭṭ*, and similarly "on the side of the raised," *fī jānib al-rafʿ*. The degrees are "the middle ones," *al-wāsiṭa*.[31] Ibn Labbān used the term "raised" (indirectly denoting the power or exponent of an order) only for integers. For fractions he used *lafẓ*, "mark," "expression," "gleaning." The meaning is close to that of "exponent." He used *lafẓ zawj* for "even mark" and *lafẓ farad* for "odd mark." *Lafẓ* served as a more general word than minutes, seconds, thirds, etc. With this distinction, between "mark" and "raised," and with a system of red and black notation, ibn Labbān had more than the germ of the idea of exponents. But the next step, to a clear exposition of exponents, did not take place

[31] Luckey, *Die Rechenkunst*, p. 67.

until much later. The question of exponents is taken up more fully later in this introduction.

Al-Qalaṣādī indicated the exponent by the word *ass*, "foundation." Al-Kāshī used *ass*, but also used *'adād al-manzila*, "numbers of the place position," for integers, and *'adād al-martaba*, "numbers of the order," for fractional orders.

In the sections using the sexagesimal tables ibn Labban uses *'adād al-'arḍ* for "numbers of the width," and *'adād al-ṭūl* for "numbers of the length."

The word "number," *'adad*, also appears in ibn Labbān with the meaning of exponent, often in connection with the difference between exponents, whether integral or fractional: "On the division of a fraction with a smaller mark by one with a larger one. The degree is raised by the numbers (*'adād*) between the marks of the dividend and divisor, as minutes by thirds is a degree raised twice, and thirds by fourths is a degree raised once."

In marking off the numerals of amounts whose roots or cube roots are taken, ibn Labbān used the words *munṭaq* and *aṣamm* for the digits marked off. These words were used by the Arabic translators of Euclid to translate his terms "rational" and "irrational," respectively, but it seems clear that ibn Labbān was not using the words in the conventional Euclidean sense. Ibn Labbān seems to mean by *munṭaq* the digits that determine the number of place positions in the resulting square root or cube root, that is, the first digit, counting from the right, of each group of two digits for square root (see page 64) or three digits for cube root (see page 100), and by *aṣamm* the remaining digits of each group. Because of the difficulty of finding English equivalents for these words that would not be impossibly confusing, a direct translation of *munṭaq* and *aṣamm* has been avoided in the text.

The terminology in the Hebrew commentary is of interest because it shows that as late as the fifteenth century mathematicians were still making up technical terms for their translations. 'Anābī tried to explain the terms he used for the Arabic cognates. *Jadr* in Judaeo-Arabic is equated with Hebrew *shōresh*. The *tanṣīf* is halving while the fractional part of sexagesimals is *alqūshūr* in Judaeo-Arabic (from the Arabic *al-kusūr*, "the fractions"), and *yitrōn* in Hebrew. The integral part of sexagesimals in Judaeo-Arabic is *sikhakh*. The Arabic terms *munṭaq* and *aṣamm* discussed in the paragraph above, are respectively *medaberet* and *elemet* in Hebrew. The remainder of the remainder, or fraction of the fraction, in Hebrew is *yitrōn ha-yitrōn*. Unfortunately, the Hebrew commentary does not take up the second book of the text, and so the most interesting terms relating to exponents and sexagesimal reckoning can not be compared with the Arabic.

Fundamental Operations of ibn Labbān

We shall here consider the fundamental operations in ibn Labbān's arithmetic, explaining them briefly and using examples from the text. However, for the purpose of clarification and simplification, we shall discuss sexagesimal methods directly after the decimal methods for each operation, instead of treating the sexagesimal system using the tables separately as does ibn Labbān in his Book II.

Addition and Subtraction of Integral Decimal Numbers

In addition, one sets down the augend and under it the addend, units under units, tens under tens, etc. As for example:

```
5 6 2 5
  8 3 9
```

The addition then begins on the left, the 8 of the lesser number being added to the 6 of the larger number above. When the result is, as in this case, more than 10, the 1 of the 10 is added to the numeral to the left above it, in this case the 5.[32] The 5 is changed to a 6, and the 6 above the 8 is altered to a 4, so that the problem is now written:

```
6 4 2 5
  8 3 9
```

Then the next orders to the right are added, and so forth. At each stage in the addition, the digits in the top row are erased and changed, as was necessary when using a dust board or waxed tablet. Kūshyār does not treat of the addition of more than two summands at a time.

The process for subtraction is the same, the larger number being placed above and the lesser below. Subtraction begins from the left, and the digits in the upper row are altered at each step. [33]

The procedures for addition and subtraction remained the same for over a thousand years, except for the special operation of halving, which the Hebrew commentary quotes ibn Labbān as calling *tanṣīf*. The description of this process is missing in the Arabic manuscript but is found in the commentary.[34] Here the operation begins on the right, which is contrary to the usual process in subtraction. However, if halving of an odd number began on the left, the procedure would become

[32] Arabic text, fol. 268b.
[33] Arabic text, fol. 269a; Hebrew text, fol. 41a.
[34] Hebrew text, fol. 41b.

more complex at the right end. If one wishes to halve 5625, he begins by halving the right-hand 5, to get 2 ½. This is then written:

5	6	2	2
		3	0[35]

because 30 is half of 60 in the sexagesimal system,[36] and ibn Labbān gives all his fractions as sexagesimals. One then proceeds to the next order to the left, and so forth.

Addition and Subtraction of Sexagesimal Numbers

This subject is not taken up in the Hebrew commentary, but it is to be found in Book II of the Arabic.[37] Here, ibn Labbān uses an example of degrees and minutes.[38] The summands are set down side by side, degrees at the top, then minutes, then seconds, as follows:

48	25
35	33
15	24

One then adds the 25 to the 48, the 33 to the 35, and so forth. When the number 60 is exceeded in one place position, a 1 is added to the place position above. The result, therefore, is written:

1	
14	25
08	33
39	24

Subtraction is carried out in a fairly similar manner. Kūshyār uses the same numbers and commences the operation with 48 minus 25, then continues to the end to give 23 1 51. The only difficulty, that of subtracting 24 from 15, is taken care of in the text by subtracting 1 from the place position before it and adding 60 (35 15 becomes 34 75) to the place position which requires it.[39]

[35] Arabic text, fols. 269a-269b.
[36] This is how a mixed decimal-sexagesimal number, having a decimal integer plus a sexagesimal fraction, often came about.
[37] Sections 3 and 4 for addition and subtraction.
[38] Arabic text, fol. 275b.
[39] Arabic text, fol. 275b.

Halving in the sexagesimal system is also written vertically:

25
36
23

Ibn Labbān begins the operation with the lowest order, just as in the decimal system, and halves the bottom 3, then its 10, then the 6 and its 10, and so forth.[40] He converts 23 to 22 60, and 25 36 to 24 96, so that the result of halving is 12 48 11 30.

Kūshyār's procedure for addition, subtraction, and halving of sexagesimals was followed by most succeeding Muslim mathematicians. Sibṭ, in the sixteenth century, worked in the same manner. However, al-Kāshī, in the fifteenth century, began his sexagesimal addition with the lowest, rather than highest, order.

Multiplication and Division of Decimal Numbers

Kūshyār has divided the section on multiplication of decimal numbers into (1) integral multiplication, and (2) multiplication of amounts having degrees and fractions (mixed decimal-sexagesimal).

The multiplier is placed under the multiplicand as in this figure:[41]

		3	2	5
2	4	3		

Each of the orders of the multiplier is multiplied by the 3 of the multiplicand. First $3 \cdot 2 = 6$, which is placed above the 2 to give:

6		3	2	5
2	4	3		

Then $3 \cdot 4 = 12$, whose 1 is added to the 6; then the resulting 7 is placed over the 2, and the 2 set in the space above the 4 to give:

7	2	3	2	5
2	4	3		

Then $3 \cdot 3 = 9$, which replaces the 3 of the multiplicand to give:

7	2	9	2	5
2	4	3		

[40] Arabic text, fol. 276a.
[41] Arabic text, fols. 269b, 270a; Hebrew text, fol. 42b.

Then the multiplier is shifted one place to the right, and the process is repeated with the 2 of the multiplicand to give:

7 7 7 6 5
2 4 3

Finally, the multiplier is moved once more to the right and multiplied by the 5, to give:

7 8 9 7 5
2 4 3

The multiplier is usually retained, as in the figure—probably a vestigial step from division, where the divisor is, and sometimes must be, kept. It also reflects the necessities imposed by the dust board. Kūshyār and later his pupil al-Nasawī were two of the finest exponents of dust board reckoning in this early period. Although permanent writing would seem to be but a short step from this, hundreds of years elapsed before it was fully established as the more desirable method. By the time of al-Kāshī, however, there was no longer any question of the value of writing, and al-Kāshī himself, in his great work,[42] uses only a permanently written form of calculation.

In the second part of his section on decimal multiplication, Kūshyār discusses the procedure for multiplying numbers having degrees and minutes. This is accomplished by converting the degrees to the type of unit in the "last" (smallest) fractional order. He does this step by step—degrees to minutes, total minutes to seconds, etc.—and the one final resulting fraction[43] is then multiplied by the other.[44] The determination of the proper orders of the product is discussed later, under our section on exponents.

The process for division is, once again, an excellent example of ibn Labbān's dust board method. For 5, 6 2 5 divided by 2 4 3, the figure is (with the largest order of each, dividend and divisor, aligned on the left):

5 6 2 5	dividend
2 4 3	divisor

One is then instructed to find a number which, when multiplied by each order of the divisor, may be subtracted from each respective order of the dividend. The number in this case is 2 and is set down thus:

[42] His *Miftāḥ al-ḥisāb*, ed. by B. A. Rozenfeld, V. S. Segal, and A. P. Yushkevich. Commentary by Yushkevich and Rozenfeld (Moscow, 1956).

[43] Arabic text, fol. 270b; Hebrew text, fol. 44a.

[44] I.e. the integral number equivalent to the sexagesimal fractional number.

		2	
5	6	2	5
2	4	3	

One then multiplies it by the 2 in the divisor, subtracts the resulting 4 from the 5 above, and moves on to the next order of the divisor, altering the digits in the dividend at each step as necessary.[45] The divisor is then shifted to the right, and the figure is:

	2	
7	6	5
2	4	3

The process continues in the above manner until the result is reached:[46]

	2	3
	3	6
2	4	3

Another part of the section on decimal division concerns the division of an integer with a fraction by another of the same kind of mixed decimal-sexagesimal. Ibn Labbān's procedure here is the same as for multiplication. The integers and fractions are converted into the units of the smallest fraction the number contains, and the "fractions" are divided by "fractions."[47]

Ibn Labbān's pupil, al-Nasawī, in his *Al-muqnī'*, also changed mixed decimal-sexagesimal numbers to the lowest denomination and, after decimal calculation, reconverted the result to a mixed decimal-sexagesimal number. Al-Birūnī (973-1048)[48] also used this method for deriving roots or powers.

Multiplication and Division of Sexagesimal Numbers

For multiplication and division of sexagesimals, Kūshyār and other medieval Arabic algorists used special tables. These are discussed later, in our section on sexagesimal tables. Unfortunately, specific knowledge of these tables is lacking, since no early examples survive.

In his example for multiplication, ibn Labbān multiplies 25 42 by

[45] Arabic text, fol. 271a; Hebrew text, fols. 44b ff.

[46] *Ibid.*

[47] Arabic text, fol. 271b. Hebrew text, fol. 47b. The "fractions" mentioned here are whole numbers which represent a certain order of sexagesimal fraction.

[48] See his *Kitāb taḥdīd nihāyāt al-amākin li-taṣḥīḥ masāfāt al-masākin*, MS Istanbul, Fatih Mosque Library 3386.

18 36. He sets these down side by side and then leaves a space between for the product:

18		25
36		42

He first uses the table to multiply the 25 by the 18. He takes the 18 in the horizontal row and 25 in the vertical and finds 7 30. He places the 7 and the 30 as follows:

	07	
18	30	25
36		42

Then he consults the table for 18 by 42, finding 12 36. The 12 is added to the 30, and the 36 placed below it. The multiplicand is then moved one place lower:

	07	
18	42	
36	36	25
		42

The process is then repeated with the 36 as the multiplier.[49]

The power of the resulting term is determined by the rules given in Section 6 of the text which, generalized, may be read as:

$$(a_i \cdot 60^i)\,(a_j \cdot 60^j) = a_j \cdot a_j \cdot 60^{i+j}$$

We discuss this further in our section of the introduction on exponents. Kūshyār gives no explanation for a 0 or -1 exponent.

For division ibn Labbān uses the table again in the problem:

4 9	1 2
3 6	2 5

The dividend is on the left in degrees and minutes, and the divisor on the right in degrees and minutes. He examines the table for 12 going down. Apposite it is 3, which gives a number less than 49 and is not likely to be too great in further multiplication of the lower orders. The product, 36, is subtracted from 49, and the 3 is marked down. Then, in the same table (for 3), apposite 25 is 1 15, and so, in modern terms:

$$3 \cdot 12 = 36$$
$$3 \cdot 25 = 75 = 1\ 15$$

$$\begin{array}{rr} 4\,9 & 3\,6 \\ -\,3\,7 & 1\,5 \\ \hline 1\,2 & 2\,1 \end{array} = \text{remainder}$$

[49] Arabic text, fol. 277a.

Shifting the divisor one place lower[50] is equivalent to adding two zeros to give a new partial dividend for more precise work. The calculation is continued as with the first step of the division. In more modern notation, the mathematics of the text is:

		12 25	12 21 00	
12 · 59	from the table		11 48	
			33 00	
25 · 59	from the table		24 35	
			8 25	remainder

The answer is 3 59 with a remainder of 8 25. In the text, the final figure is

0 3	0 0	
5 9	0 8	1 2
	2 5	2 5

Ibn Labbān explains that when the first place position is not divisible by the divisor, one sets down a zero in place of the result and then shifts the divisor without having changed it.

In Kūshyār's next section of the text he gives the rules for the results of division. Since these are concerned with the rules for exponents, we discuss them under that heading later in this introduction. However, the general rule, in modern terminology, may be given as

$$\frac{a_i \cdot 60^i}{a_j \cdot 60^j} = \frac{a_i}{a_j} \cdot 60^{i-j}$$

In the Arabic text, this rule was broken up into more specific ones that were easier to employ when working rhetorically or on a dust board.

The use of pure sexagesimal reckoning was rare with Muslim mathematicians. It was not uncommon in the medieval period to convert a sexagesimal number to a decimal for simpler operation, especially in multiplication and division. The dividend, when smaller than the divisor, was frequently multiplied by 60 until it was larger than the divisor. Furthermore, Kūshyār, in Book I of this text, does not hesitate to convert an integral amount together with sexagesimal fractions to the lowest order of the sexagesimal for easier working. These conversions were common also with such a medieval mathematician as al-Khwārizmī.[51]

[50] Arabic text, fol. 278a.

[51] See also al-Nasawī (*Al-muqniʿ fi'l-hisāb al-hindī*, MS Leiden, Rijksuniversiteit Arabic 1021, fol. 78a) who did this and then converted the result to a decimal integer with a sexagesimal fraction.

When sexagesimal reckoning was used, it most frequently was mixed with decimal calculation. The use of decimal integers and sexagesimal fractions is to be found as early as the works of Ptolemy[52] and Theon. This was true to some extent for ibn Labbān also, since he did not go higher than degrees in his sexagesimal calculation, while in his decimal mathematics his fractions were always sexagesimals. However, Kūshyār understood and demonstrated almost a pure sexagesimal procedure for all but the cube root operation.[53] This understanding is not to be found in al-Bīrūnī's *Taḥdīd*, in al-Khwārizmī, or in John of Seville, but al-Karajī (early eleventh century) demonstrated it in his multiplication. As late as the fourteenth century, Levi ben Gerson did not understand complete sexagesimal calculation.[54] Much later, al-Kāshī (fifteenth century) and Sibṭ al-Māridīnī[55] (early sixteenth century) knew it. Sibṭ's system for sexagesimal multiplication is shown in the example below for 20 30 40 by 5 10:[56]

1	45	58	26	40
1	40			
	2	30		
		3	20	
	3	20		
		5	0	
			6	40
	5	0		
		20	30	40
	20	30	40	

Explanation:

		20	30	40	
		5	10		
1	40				= 5 · 20
	2	30			= 5 · 30
		3	20		= 5 · 40
	3	20			= 10 · 20
		5	0		= 10 · 30
			6	40	= 10 · 40
1	45	58	26	40	

First, the 5 is multiplied by every term of the multiplicand; then the 10 is also multiplied in the same way. The partial products are written down and spaced out carefully with regard to the powers of 60, then finally added to give the product above. The tables are used throughout.

In division, Sibṭ gives the example of 42 30 divided by 1 25. His process is quite similar to that of ibn Labbān, including the use of the

[52] Claudius Ptolemaeus, *Syntaxis mathematica*, ed. Johan Heiberg (Leipzig, 1898-1903); Theon of Alexandria, in Nicholas Halma's edition of the *Almagest* (Paris, 1816-1820).

[53] C. Schoy, *Isis*, 5, 364-399 (1923).

[54] *Levi ben Gerschom, Sefer Maassei Choscheb. Die Praxis des Rechners*, ed. and transl. Gerson Lange (Frankfurt am Main, 1909).

[55] Died 1527. Astronomer and mathematician. Wrote *Raqā'iq al-haqā'iq fī ḥisāb al-daraj wa'l-daqā'iq*, MS Gotha, 1390, Herzoglichen Bibliothek "Five Points of the Truths in the Calculation of Degrees and Minutes."

[56] Luckey, *Die Rechenkunst*, p. 69.

tables. As with the multiplication, only his arrangement of putting down the partial and final results differs from that of ibn Labbān.

Square Root and Approximative Methods for Non-Squares in ibn Labbān and Other Algorists

Ibn Labbān discusses square root in two sections of his treatise: in the eighth section of the first book and again in the ninth section of the second book. In the first of these sections he takes the root of 65342 as follows:[57]

1. Mark off the digits by two's beginning on the right; then 6 is left over:

$$6\ 5\ 3\ 4\ 2 = q$$

2. The largest square into 6 is 4. Subtract it from 6 to give 2. The process was carried out on a dust board so that the 2 was put in place of the 6 to give:

$$2\ 5\ 3\ 4\ 2$$

3. The root is 2 (upper) and a 2 remains:

$$\begin{array}{lll} 2 & & a \\ 2\ 5\ 3\ 4\ 2 & & a^2 \leq 6(5342), \quad a^2 = 4(0000) \\ 2 & & \end{array}$$

4. Double the lower 2 and move it one order to the right:

$$\begin{array}{lr} \ \ 2 & \\ 2\ 5\ 3\ 4\ 2 & q - a^2 \\ \ \ 4 & 2a = 4 \end{array}$$

5. Then obtain a number such that when it is multiplied by itself, then by 4, the product can be subtracted from 253; it is 5:

$$\begin{array}{lr} \ \ 2\ 5 & b = 5 \\ 2\ 5\ 3\ 4\ 2 & \\ \ \ 4\ 5 & 2a + b \end{array}$$

$$(2a + b)b \leq q - a^2$$

or

$$(40 + 5)5 = 225 < 253$$

6. Multiply 45 by 5 and subtract it from 253; 28 remains:

$$\begin{array}{l} \ \ 2\ 5 \\ 2\ 8\ 4\ 2 \\ \ \ 4\ 5 \end{array}$$

[57] Arabic text, fol. 272b; Hebrew text, fol. 48b.

This process is repeated until the root is obtained. Kūshyār's pupil, al-Nasawī,[58] uses exactly the same process. In modern equivalents, this problem is solved:

		2 5 5	
		6 53 42	
$a^2 = 2^2 = 4$		4	
$2a = 4, \quad b = 5$	45	2 53	
$2(10a) + b = 45$		2 25	
$2(100a + 10b) = 500$	505	28 42	
$2(100a + 10b) + c = 505$		25 25	
		3 17	remainder.

Much later, Georg von Peurbach (1423-61), who had studied under Nicholas of Cusa and other well-known mathematicians, wrote an arithmetic[59] in which he used, with minor variations, the same method for square root determination as Kūshyār. He used a more modern form of writing than the dust board, and his procedure is very close to the methods of today, as may be seen from the following example:

Write the amount and mark the first, third, and fifth numerals as uneven positions by means of a dot above them. Then the sought after amount will have as many places as there are points. Begin with the last designated position and seek a number which when multiplied by itself will equal or be as large as possible without being greater than that dotted digit with the one before it [if there is one]. Such digits may, at the most, be 9 and, in the least, be 1. Then write it as in division at the right of our amount with a line drawn before it [i.e. the amount]. Multiply it by itself and subtract the product from its proper position. Cross out this [position] and write the remainder above. Double the found digit and write the doubled one under the next numeral to the right of the position just used.

$$\begin{array}{lllll|l} 2 & & & & & \\ \dot{6} & 6 & \dot{0} & 4 & \dot{9} & 2 \\ & 4 & & & & \end{array}$$

[58] *Al-muqniʿ fi'l-ḥisāb al-hindī*, MS cited, fol. 72b. See also Suter, *Bibl. Math.*, Ser. III, **7**, 113-19 (1906).

[59] *Elementa arithmetices algorithmus de numeris integris* (first printed 1492). See P. Treutlein, *Abhandlungen zur Geschichte der Mathematik*, 1, 64-65 (1877).

Then search under the zero before the doubled one for a digit of such quantity that when it is multiplied by the doubled one and then squared, then [the sum] will either be equal to or come as close as possible to the partial radicand [which includes the remainder and the next set of positions]. Write down the digit before the previously determined one. [Carry out the multiplications and subtraction and set down the remainder above. Cross out the next set after the 6].

$$\begin{array}{ccccccc} 2 & 3 & 5 & & & & \\ \dot{6} & 6 & \dot{0} & 4 & \dot{9} & | & 2\ 5 \\ & 4 & & & & & \\ 2 & 2 & 5 & & & & \end{array}$$

Then double the above determined digits [25] and put this doubled number under the next numeral right of the position where it was found, and back of the previous doubling, one position farther. The first doubling also moves one position to the right. If, in the second doubling, it is over 9, then add this as articulus to the previous doubling. . . .

$$\begin{array}{ccccc} 2 & 3 & 5 & & \\ \dot{6} & 6 & \dot{0} & 4 & \dot{9} \\ & & 5 & 0 & \\ & 3 & 5 & 4 & 9 \end{array}$$

In the determination of the square root of a non-square, the final approximative process for the remainder is important. Ibn Labbān employed the procedure of adding pairs of zeros to obtain a more exact answer in decimal work. He also used an approximative method for the root of A which is the sum of $a^2 + r$ giving $a + r/(2a + 1)$. The r is the remainder of the radicand. Al-Nasawī used this same procedure.

Ibn Labbān's formula comes about as follows:

If $A = a^2 + r$, then

$$a_1 = a + \frac{r}{2a}.$$

Then

$$\frac{A}{a_1} = a + \frac{r}{2a + r/a}$$

where a_1, the arithmetic mean, is equal to $\frac{1}{2}(a + A/a)$, and is an approximation of the second order by excess. The harmonic mean, A/a_1, is an approximation of the second order by defect. This procedure is subject to further refinement. Since a_1 also equals $a + r/2a$, an approximation by excess, then

$$a_1' = a + \frac{r}{2a + 1},$$

an approximation by defect. This approximation was well known to the Arabs but not to the Greeks.[60]

Abū Zakarīyā al-Ḥaṣṣār (*ca.* 1175)[61] also approximated his remainder after the determination of the square root. In general terms, his method is more advanced than that used by al-Qalaṣādī, who lived much later (d. 1486) and wrote a commentary on ibn al-Bannā''s arithmetic.[62] Al-Qalaṣādī used

$$a + \frac{r+1}{2a+2}$$

Al-Ḥaṣṣār takes the root of the next higher square and subtracts from it the quotient of the remainder $(a+1)^2 - (a^2 + r)$ by means of the double of the root which comes out:

$$(a+1) - \frac{2a+1-r}{2(a+1)} = a + \frac{r+1}{2a+2}$$

The second approximation[63] is:

$$\sqrt{a^2+r} = a + \frac{r}{2a} - \frac{(r/2a)^2}{2(a + r/2a)}$$

Estienne de la Roche (*ca.* 1520),[64] a pupil of Chuquet, in his discussion of approximative procedure gives: $\sqrt{6}$ = a value from 2 to 3. So, he probes $2\frac{1}{2}$ which is too much, then $2\frac{1}{3}$ which is too little, then 2 plus the interpolated fractions: $\frac{2}{5}, \frac{3}{7}, \frac{4}{9}, \frac{5}{11}, \frac{9}{20}, \frac{13}{29}, \frac{31}{69}, \frac{40}{89}, \frac{49}{109}, \frac{89}{198}$. These are insufficient. He finally comes to $2\frac{881}{1960}$, where the error is 1 in 3,841,600.

[60] Paul Tannery, *Bibl. Math.*, Ser. II, **1**, 17 (1878); see D. E. Smith, *History of Mathematics* (Boston, 1925), **2**, 253-5. For further information regarding approximation, see Hochheim, *Kāfī fi'l ḥisāb* (Magdeburg, 1878-79), **2**, 14; Gustav Wertheim, *Die Arithmetik des Elia Misrachi* (Frankfurt am Main, 1893), p. 21; Baldassarre Boncompagni, *Atti dell'Accademia pontificia de' Nuovi Lincei*, **12**, 402 (1859).

[61] Suter, *Bibl. Math.*, Ser. III, **2**, 37 (1901). Al-Ḥaṣṣār's text is also to be found in the Hebrew translation of Moses ibn Tibbon (1271), MS, Vatican Hebrew 396 and MS Oxford, Christ Church 189. It is divided into two books, on integers, and on fractions. The dust board is still used in this text. Ibn al-Bannā' (1256-1321), in his *Talkhīṣ fī a'māl al-ḥisāb*, is deeply indebted to al-Ḥaṣṣār.

[62] *Sharḥ talkhīṣ ibn al-Bannā'*, MS Gotha, Herzoglichen Bibliothek 1477. See Aristide Marre, *Atti de' Nuovi Lincei* (1865), **17**, 289-319 for a French translation of ibn al-Bannā'; for extract from al-Qalasādī' commentary, see *J. asiat.*, **1**, 58-62 (1863).

[63] See Moritz Benedikt Cantor, *Vorlesungen über Geschichte der Mathematik*, 2nd ed. (Leipzig, 1894), **1**, 765; Franz Woepcke, *Atti dell'Accad. pontif. de' Nuovi Lincei*, **12**, 41 (1859).

[64] *Larismethique nouellement composee par maistre Estienne de la roche dict Villefranche natif de Lyō* (Lyons, 1520); see Nicolas Chuquet's "Triparty en la Science des Nombres" in *Boncompagni's Bullettino*, **13**, 555 (1880); Ch. Lambo, "Une algèbre Française de 1484. Nicolas Chuquet," *Revue des Questions Scientifiques* (Brussels, 1902).

We have been considering until now only the methods used for finding the root of an integer. However, Kūshyār ibn Labbān also discusses means for determining the root of an integer plus fractions :

If we wish the root of an integer plus fractions, we convert the integer plus fractions to the category of the last fraction that it has. Then when we see that the mark of the fraction is even, we extract its root. When the [mark of the] fraction is odd, we multiply it by 60 once again so that it is converted to a fraction with an even mark. Then its root is extracted, and if what remains of the square is zeros preceded by no number, take half of those zeros and put them before the resulting root.[65]

From the quotation, it is evident that by fraction ibn Labbān meant the sexagesimal fraction. The integer alone was considered in the decimal manner. The problem is then reduced to one in decimal arithmetic with the entire number being changed to the term having the most negative exponent.

In the ninth section of the second book the Arabic text shows the extraction of the root of 45° 36′ and when the work is slightly rearranged the steps in this operation are more easily understood in relation to the modern method:

	6 45 9
	———
	45 36 00
	36
	———
12	9 36
	9
	———
	0 36 00
	33 45
	———
13 30	2 15 00
	1 57
	———
	18 00
	4 30
	———
	13 30 00
$9^2 = 1\ 21$	1 21
	———
	13 28 39

1. First the largest square less than or equal to 45 is determined and set down, then subtracted from 45.
2. The partial root is doubled to give 12.
3. 12 is multiplied by 45, a new partial answer, to give 9.
4. The partial answer 45, multiplied by itself is 33 45. The 9 and 33 45 are subtracted in turn.
5. The 6 45 is doubled to give 13 30.
6. First 13 is multiplied by 9, a new partial answer, to give 1 57.
7. Then 30 is multiplied by 9, giving 4 30.
8. The 1 57 and 4 30 are subtracted in turn.
9. The 9 is squared to give 1 21 which is subtracted.

[65] Arabic text, fol. 273b. This is not found in the Hebrew text.

Al-Nasawī shows an advance, although small, over ibn Labbān in the determination of roots of fractions and mixed numbers. In sexagesimal fractions, he changes degrees, minutes, and seconds, etc., to the even seconds, and fourths and derives the roots therefrom. For example:

$$\sqrt{26\quad 7} = \frac{1}{60}\sqrt{94{,}020} = \frac{1}{60}\cdot 307 = 5\quad 7$$

He also operates with powers of 10, such as:

$$\sqrt{17} = \frac{1}{100}\sqrt{170{,}000} = \frac{1}{100}\cdot 412 = 4\quad 7\ 12$$

In the case of a fraction which is a square, he determines the square root directly without resort to the sexagesimal method. Examples are:

$$\sqrt{30\,\tfrac{1}{4}} = \sqrt{\frac{121}{4}} = \frac{11}{2} = 5\,\tfrac{1}{2}$$

$$\sqrt{\tfrac{1}{4}} = \tfrac{1}{2}$$

Al-Nasawī also gives two similar problems in the cube root operation (see note 58):

$$\sqrt[3]{\tfrac{1}{8}} = \tfrac{1}{2}$$

$$\sqrt[3]{3\,\tfrac{3}{8}} = \sqrt[3]{\tfrac{27}{8}} = \tfrac{3}{2} = 1\,\tfrac{1}{2}$$

Neither these examples nor similar methods are to be found in ibn Labbān's work or in the Hebrew commentary.

As yet, no Latin translation of al-Nasawī's treatise has been found, and so it is uncertain how and through whom he and ibn Labbān influenced the West, separately from the works of later Arabic mathematicians.[66] In connection with fractional operations, al-Nasawī's work is of a much simpler nature than that of such later western Arabic mathematicians as al-Ḥaṣṣār (twelfth century) and al-Qalaṣādī (d. 1486). The work of ibn Labbān and al-Nasawī also differed significantly from that of their near contemporary, al-Karajī (d. 1012-29), in that they employed Hindu numerals, while he used no numerals at all.

[66] See G. Eneström's surmise in *Bibl. Math.*, Ser. III, **7**, 24-37 (1906) where he discusses the *Demonstratio Jordani de algorismo* of the Cod. Dresd. Db. 86, probably by Jordanus Nemorarius. Another copy of Jordanus' text but quite different is in P. Duhem's "Sur l'algorithmus demonstratus," *Bibl. Math.*, Ser. III, **6**, 9-15 (1905). Jordanus did not know al-Nasawī but knew of other Arabic writings.

Cube Root and Approximative Methods for the Non-cube

The following is a concise, step-by-step, non-rhetorical account of ibn Labbān's method:

1. Mark off the digits by three's, beginning on the right:

   2′986′100

2. Place a row of zeros below the number. The largest root equal to or less than the left hand group is 1.

3. Place the 1 as follows:

1	$= a$	top row
2986100		amount row
0000000		middle row
1		bottom row

4. The top 1 times the bottom 1 = 1. Add this to the middle:

   1
   2986100
   1000000
   1

5. Subtract the middle from the quantity which was given:

   1
   1986100
   1000000
   1

6. Double the bottom number. Then multiply the top 1 by the bottom 1 doubled and add the product to the middle:

   1
   1986100
   3000000
   2

7. Add the top 1 to the bottom 2 to give 3:

   1
   1986100
   3000000
   3

8. Shift the middle one place position and the bottom two place positions to the right:

```
 1
 1986100
  300000
    3
```

These shifts automatically preserve the proper place positions in the various operations in relation to the upper rows. The next figure in the answer is determined so as to satisfy the crucial operation of the important subtraction from the remaining partial quantity. Thus, steps three to eight are repeated for the second figure of the answer in steps nine to twelve, and in steps thirteen to sixteen for the third.

9. Determine the proper figure by trial. The method of trial is not given in the text. The figure sought is 4, and is so placed:

```
1 4          b = 4
1986100
 300000
   34
```

10. Multiply the top 4 by the bottom orders: $4 \cdot 34 = 136$. Add the 136 to the middle: $136 + 300 = 436$:

```
1 4          a = 10;  b = 4.
1986100
 436          = 3a² + (3a + b) b
  34          = 3a + b
```

11. Multiply the top 4 by the new middle and subtract the result from the partial quantity (or cube): $4 \cdot 436 = 1744$; $1986 - 1744 = 242$:

```
1 4
 242100    b[3a² + (3a + b) b] = 3a²b + 3ab² + b³
 436000
   34
```

12. Double the lowest 4 to give 38 on the bottom. Multiply it by 4. Then $38 \cdot 4 = 152$. Add this to the middle; $436 + 152 = 588$. Shift the middle row one place position, and shift the bottom row two place positions. Add the highest 4 to the lowest on the right: $38 + 4 = 42$:

```
1 4
 242100
  58800    3a² + 3ab + b² + (3a + 2b) b = 3a² + 6ab + 3b²
                                        = 3(a + b)²
    42     42 = 3(a + b) = 3(10 · 1 + 4)
```

13. The next desired figure is 4. Place it on the top and bottom:

$$\begin{array}{rl} 1\ \ 4\ \ 4 & a = 100;\quad b = 40;\quad c = 4. \\ 242100 & \\ 58800 & = 3(a+b)^2 \\ 424 & = 3(a+b)+c \end{array}$$

14. Multiply the last 4 on the top by the bottom orders: $4 \cdot 424 = 1696$. Add the 1696 to the middle: $1696 + 58{,}800 = 60{,}496$:

$$\begin{array}{rl} 1\ \ 4\ \ 4 & \\ 242100 & \\ 60496 & = 3(a+b)^2 + 3(a+b)\,c + c^2 \\ 424 & = 3(a+b)+c \end{array}$$

15. Multiply the last top 4 by the new middle, then subtract it from the partial quantity: $4 \cdot 60496 = 241984$; $242100 - 241984 = 116$:

$$241984 = 3(a+b)^2\,c + 3(a+b)\,c^2 + c^3$$

$$\begin{array}{rl} 1\ \ 4\ \ 4 & \\ 116 & \\ 60496 & \\ 424 & = 3(a+b)+c \end{array}$$

16. Double the right bottom 4 to get 428. Then $428 \cdot 4 = 1712$. Add this to the middle: $60496 + 1712 = 62208$:

$$\begin{array}{rl} 1\ \ 4\ \ 4 & \\ 116 & \\ 62208 & = 3(a+b+c)^2 \\ 428 & = 3(a+b)+c+c \end{array}$$

17. Add one to the middle at the right end to give 62209. The last partial quantity is the remainder which may be converted to the sexagesimal fractions as thirds, sixths, and ninths to obtain a more precise cube root.

Various procedures based on the same identity,

$$(a+b) = \sqrt[3]{a^3 + 3a^2b + 3ab^2 + b^3}$$

may be used to derive the cube root. Al-Nasawī's method, however, is very similar to that of ibn Labbān. Only a slight difference exists between these two, mainly in the more abbreviated character of al-Nasawī's arithmetic. In the square root, for example, the pupil obtains the sum of $2ab$ and b^2 directly, while ibn Labbān gets $2a$, then adds it to b, then multiplies the sum by b to get $(2a + b)\,b$. The same abbreviations take place in the process for the cube root. For example, instead of proceeding by small steps, al-Nasawī reckons $[3a^2 + (3a + b)\,b]\,b$ at one time, then he subtracts. This is an example of the general tightening up which developed in the basic processes throughout the period of medieval Islamic mathematics.

Al-Nasawī,[67] in obtaining the cube root of 3,652,296, first marks off the amount, three places at a time, going toward the left, and then proceeds as follows:

1. Put the root of 3, which is 1, over the 3 and under it twice. Subtract 1 from the 3 [in the amount:]

```
1
2652296
1
1
```

2. Double the 1 of the lowest row. Then multiply the uppermost 1 by the 2. This product is added to the 1 of the third row. Then the uppermost 1 is added to the 2 of the fourth. The 3 of the third row is moved one place and the lowest row two places to the right:

```
1
2652296
 3
  3
```

3. "Then one seeks a number such that when one multiplies it by the lowest 3 and by itself, and these two products are added to the number of the third row, and this sum is multiplied by the determined number, and then this product is subtracted from the radicand remainder, then [the remainder obtained is either zero or there is another remainder]." This number is 5. Put it behind the 3 of the lowest row, and in the uppermost over the 2. Then multiply it by the lowest 3 and square it. Add this product, then add the sum to the 3 of the third row. Multiply the whole by the 5 which was found, and subtract the product from the remainder to give:

```
1 5
 277296     new remainder of the radicand.
 475
  35
```

[67] See al-Nasawī, MS cited, fols. 73a-73b; (for details of MS, see note 58.) See also Suter, *Bibl. Math.*, Ser. III, **7**, 115-17.

4. Double the lowest 5. Add it to the 3 [30] before it to give 40. Multiply it by the uppermost 5 and add it to the 475 [to give 675]. Add the uppermost 5 to the [40] in the lowest row [to give 45], then move the third row one position, and the fourth two places to the right:[68]

```
1 5
 277296⁶⁹
  675
     45
```

A third number is sought in the same manner. The next two figures given are:

```
1  5  4
     32
  69316
    454

1  5  4
     32
  71149
    462
```

In this last figure, 32 is the new remainder.

$$69316 = 3(a + b)^2 + 3(a + b)\, c + c^2$$
$$454 = 3(a + b) + c$$

From 277296 subtract

$$69316 \cdot 4 = 277264 = 3(a + b)^2\, c + 3(a + b)\, c^2 + c^3$$

Al-Nasawī's text gives the remaining fraction as

$$\frac{32}{71149} = \frac{r}{3(a + b + c)^2 + 1}$$

However, he must have known that the r is part of two successive cubes $(a + 1)^3$ and a^3; to distinguish the $3a^2 + 3a + 1$, he should have said that the remainder 32 is made up of the third and fourth rows together. Correctly, it is:

$$\frac{32}{71149 + 462} = \frac{32}{71611} = \frac{r}{3(a + b + c)^2 + 3(a + b + c) + 1}$$

[68] $675 = 475 + 200 = 3a^2 + 3ab + b^2 + (3a + 2b)\, b = 3a^2 + 6ab + 3b^2 = 3(a + b)^2$ or $45 = 3(a + b)$.

[69] When $a = 10$ and $b = 5$, then $35 = 3a + b$; multiply 475 by b to give 2375; $2375 = 3a^2b + 3ab^2 + b^3$. Subtract this from 2652 to give 277.

The Hebrew commentary on ibn Labbān's work gives the remainder as 428 parts of the sum of 62208 plus 1. The 428 is called *alqūshūr* in Judaeo-Arabic, from *kusūr* "parts" in Arabic. It is evident that neither ibn Labbān nor his pupil approximated more finely in the cube root process.

Leonardo Fibonacci used the following second approximation:

$$\sqrt[3]{n} = \sqrt{a^3 + r} = a + \frac{r}{3a^2 + 3a + 1} = a_1$$

and further

$$a_2 = a_1 + \frac{n - a_1^3}{3a_1(a + 1)} \quad {}^{70}$$

This approximation was probably original with Leonardo.

Heron[71] is said to have used an approximation for cube root:

$$\sqrt[3]{n} = b + \frac{a(n - b^3)}{n + a(n - b^3)} \qquad a > \sqrt[3]{n} > b, \quad a - b = 1$$

Since there have been questions as to Heron's meaning in his discussion of this subject, the following is a translation of his text:

> Approximation to the cube root of a non-cube. Take the nearest cube numbers to 100 both above and below; these are 125 and 64. Then 125 − 100 = 25, and 100 − 64 = 36. Multiply 5 by 36; this gives 180. Add 100, making 280. [Divide 180 by 280]; this gives $\frac{9}{14}$. Add this to the side of the smaller cube: this gives $4\frac{9}{14}$. This is as nearly as possible the cube root of 100 units.[72]

G. Wertheim, according to Heath, has worked out the best formula:

If $a^3 < A < (a + 1)^3$ and $A - a^3 = d_1$, $(a + 1)^3 - A = d_2$,

then the approximate cube root is:

$$a + \frac{(a + 1)\,d_1}{(a + 1)\,d_1 + ad_2}$$

G. Eneström has given a simple explanation of the derivation of the cube root as Heron has used it.[73]

[70] "Note to Cantor's *Vorlesungen*," by Heinrich Suter, *Bibl. Math.*, Ser. III, **6**, 105 (1905); see also Fibonacci, *Liber abaci di Leonardo Pisano* (written 1202), in *Scritti di Leonardo Pisano*, ed. Baldassarre Boncampagni (Rome, 1857) **1**, 380-82.

[71] Thomas L. Heath, *History of Greek Mathematics* (Oxford, 1921), **2**, 341-42.

[72] *Ibid.*, p. 341.

[73] In Suter, "Small Notes to Cantor's *Vorlesungen*," *Bibl. Math.*, Ser. III, **8**, 412-13 (1907-8); see also Heath, *Hist. Greek Math.*

Ibn Labbān adds groups of three zeros to obtain a more exact cube root. This was also done by Cardanus (1539), Gemma Frisius (1540), and by Ramus (1555). Cardanus sets the first approximation as:

$$\sqrt[3]{a^3 + r} = a + \frac{r}{3a^2}$$

It is cubed and then the surplus over $(a^3 + r)$ is divided by $3a^2$ to get

$$\frac{r_1}{3a^2}$$

The latter is subtracted from the former approximation to get the second approximation:[74]

$$a + \frac{r}{3a^2} - \frac{r_1}{3a^2}$$

The Checking Operation

The modulo 9 check, or "checking by nines," for decimal integers was popular with medieval Muslim mathematicians, ibn Labbān among them. For integers, he gives the procedure very simply in Book I, section 9, which is devoted entirely to arithmetic checks by casting out nines.[75]

Interestingly, Kūshyār also used the mod 9 check in his sexagesimal work.[76] To obtain the "indicator," of a sexagesimal number, as in his example, the procedure is as follows:

25	$2 + 5 \equiv 7 \bmod 9;$	$7 \cdot 6 = 42$
38	$42 + 3 + 8 = 53 \equiv 8 \bmod 9;$	$8 \cdot 6 = 48$
46	$48 + 4 + 6 = 58 \equiv 4 \bmod 9$	

The indicator equals 4. If the 25 is $25 \cdot 60^2$, then there is no reason to include that or any higher terms, 60^2 being divisible by 9. The factors of 60^2 only may be ignored, not any others. In the case of $25 \cdot 60^2$, $38 \cdot 60^1$, and $46 \cdot 60^0$, only the two orders, 38 and 46, need be reckoned. This reduces the effectiveness of the check. A further reduction in its value is due to the fact that the 38 is multiplied by 60, which already has a factor of 3.

[74] Treutlein, *Abh. Gesch. Math.*, 1, 75-76.
[75] Arabic text, fol. 274a; Hebrew text, fols. 54b-55a.
[76] Arabic text, fols. 280a-280b.

The same error is found in Sibṭ al-Māridīnī's arithmetical work, *Raqā'iq al-ḥaqā'iq fī ḥisāb al-daraj wa'l-daqā'iq.*[77] Sibṭ uses mod 7 and mod 8 procedures. In both the mod 7 and mod 8 methods, the sum of the digits in each line mod 7 (or mod 8) is multiplied by 4, then added to the digits in the next lower order. When 60 is divided by 7 or 8, the remainder is 4 in each case. For the mod 8 method a difficulty is easily seen for 60^2 and higher where 8 is a factor, analogous to the use of mod 9, as 9 is also a factor of 60^2. Sixty, also, is divisible by 4, which further weakens this checking process.

Al-Kāshī, the fifteenth-century mathematician, chose 59 for his check, which is similar to the check by nines, since $60 \equiv 1 \bmod 59$ and $10 \equiv 1 \bmod 9$.

At no time did Kūshyār state that if the checks were correct then the original operation must have been carried out correctly, although this was a commonly held belief in the medieval Muslim period. Even Sibṭ, in the sixteenth century, still held to this belief. Al-Kāshī, on the other hand, was more discerning and stated that when the calculation is correct, then the check works out, and when the check does not work out, then the calculation is not correct. Stated thus, it is clear the author understands that the errors using mod 9 or mod 59 will not show up. This was not known well enough before al-Kāshī, even by such an intelligent mathematician as Fibonacci.[78]

Fundamental Operations of Earlier and Later Algorists

It is strange that in Europe throughout the early Middle Ages the art of calculation flourished simultaneously on two levels. The first method employed an instrument, such as the abacus, or various types of tablets marked off in rows or columns.[79]

The second approach to arithmetical calculation was algorismic and was distinguished by its recognition of the zero and the fundamental operations of addition, subtraction, halving, doubling, multiplication, division, and root extraction, more or less as they are known today. This method does not preclude the use of instruments, but the rules for the algorismic method are not dependent on the particular type of memory aid in use.

[77] *Katalog der Bibliothek des Instituts für Geschichte der Medizin und der Naturwissenschaften*, **2**, 49; see C. Schoy, *Quellen und Studien zur Geschichte der Naturwissenschaften und der Medizin*, **7**, 160 (1939); Luckey, *Die Rechenkunst*, p. 71.

[78] Boncompagni, ed., *Scritti di Leonardo Pisano*, **1**, 8.

[79] Herodotus, **2**, 36; Plato, *De Legibus*, **7**; L. C. Karpinski, *Isis*, **5**, 20-25 (1923).

The term algorism is a corruption of the name of al-Khwārizmī, the early Muslim mathematician (d. *ca.* 850) whose works wielded a powerful influence upon the growth of both European and Eastern mathematics, including that of Kūshyār ibn Labbān.

The modern algorism is usually divided into the four operations of addition, subtraction, multiplication, and division. But the classification has not always been so simple. In the Middle Ages, many more operations were considered to be fundamental, as the table below shows. With time, however, many of these were sloughed off. Most of this discarding did not take place until the nineteenth century. The following listing of the fundamental operations of some medieval mathematicians indicates which ones they considered of importance.

It is also of value to know the order in which they took up the operations. In an opening statement, ibn Labbān catalogues the principles of arithmetic in three basic categories:[80] multiplication, division, and square root. As an afterthought, he adds cube root. This, however, is not the actual order of his operations in the text. In the following table are listed the fundamental operations as given by Kūshyār and other algorists, both antedating and succeeding him.[81] The operations are listed in the order in which each algorist discussed them.

Mahāvīrācārya (9th cent.)	*al-Khwārizmī* (*ca.* 820)	*ibn Labbān* (*ca.* 1000)
multiplication	numeration	numeration
division	addition	addition
square	subtraction	subtraction
square root	halving	halving
cube	doubling	multiplication
cube root	multiplication	division
summation of series	division	square root
subtraction		cube root

[80] Arabic text, fol. 267b.

[81] Benedict, *Comp. Study of Early Treatises*, p. 25; Baldassarre Boncompagni, ed., *Algoritmi de numero indorum* by al-Khwārizmī, in Latin, in *Trattati d'arithmetica* (Rome, 1857), vol. 1; Hochheim, *Kāfī fīl Hisāb* (Magdeburg, 1878-79); Martin Levey, *Osiris*, **11**, 50-63 (1954), and *Isis*, **43**, 257-64 (1952); Silberberg, ed., *Sefer Ha-Mispar*; Alfred Nagel, *Zeit. f. Math. u. Physik*, **34** (1889); Eneström, *Bibl. Math.*, Ser. III, **7**, 24-37 (1906), Ser. III, **8**, 135-53 (1907-8); Boncompagni, ed.,*Liber abaci*, in *Scritti di Leonardo Pisano*, vol. **1**; Halliwell[-Phillipps], ed., *Rara Mathematica*; Carl B. Boyer, "Fundamental Steps in the Development of Numeration," *Isis*, **35**, 153-68 (1945); Halliwell[-Phillipps], *Carmen de Algorismo*, in *Rara Mathematica*, pp. 73-83; *Levi ben Gerson, Sefer Maassei Choscheb*, ed., Lange.

al-Karajī (*ca.* 1010)	*Savasorda* (early 12th c.)	*Abraham ibn Ezra* (*ca.* 1150)
multiplication	multiplication	multiplication
" of fractions	division	division
division	subtraction	addition
" of fractions	fractions	subtraction
extraction of roots	transformation of fractions	fractions
business arithmetic	proportion	proportion
mensuration		square root

Ralph of Laon (12th cent.)	*Jordanus Nemorarius* (13th cent.)	*Leonardo Fibonacci* (1202)
numeration	addition	numeration
multiplication	subtraction	multiplication
addition	doubling	addition
subtraction	halving	subtraction
division	multiplication	division
	division	square and cube roots
	square root	

Sacrobosco (13th cent.)	*Alexandri de Villa Dei* (13th cent.)	*Levi ben Gerson* (1321)
numeration	addition	addition
addition	subtraction	subtraction
subtraction	doubling	multiplication
halving	halving	series
doubling	multiplication	permutations
multiplication	division	combinations
division	root extraction	division
progression		proportion
root extraction		square and cube roots

From this table, it may be noted that there is much variation, not only in the particular operations treated but also in their order. The operations of halving and doubling[82] are common in medieval texts until the

[82] These operations are still in use among some peoples today. See L. C. Karpinski and Frank Egleston Robbins, *Introduction to Arithmetic by Nicomachus of Gerasa* (New York, 1926), p. 8.

sixteenth century. Ibn Labbān discusses halving only; this may, however, be a textual omission of doubling. In the earliest times in Egypt both these operations were already in use.[83] The effectiveness and persistence of these two operations may be traced down through the Greeks[84] and on to al-Khwārizmī, through whom these processes, later on, reached Europe. Leonardo Fibonacci and Abraham ibn Ezra did not consider halving and doubling.

Denomination,[85] division of a smaller by a larger number, as a separate operation is found in the works of ibn Labbān, Savasorda, al-Ḥaṣṣār, ibn al-Bannā', and al-Qalaṣādī. Denomination does not appear in Hindu and Latin algorisms although the word *denominatio* was commonly used by the abacists for a quotient.

As to the order of the operations, most algorists begin with numeration, as does ibn Labbān. Others begin with multiplication. The abacists usually discussed multiplication before other operations because of its fundamental importance in their process.

Sexagesimal Tables and Their Use

The Sumerians were, as we mentioned earlier, the first to develop a sexagesimal system including both integers and fractions. It is uncertain, however, why 60 was originally chosen as a base, or how the system was preserved. The medieval manuscripts containing sexagesimal reckoning of fractions attribute the use of this system to its great convenience in astronomy and business. Ibn Labbān, for example, states at the beginning of Book II that the sexagesimal system, based on a table, makes work with fractions easier and allows for greater precision than is otherwise possible. Furthermore, he says, the sexagesimal system exists in all reckoning, in astronomical and business matters.[86]

Kūshyār's reference to astronomical and business matters suggests that it was through these activities that sexagesimal calculation was kept alive. In the medieval world, as in Babylonian times, many of the weight denominations were based on 60, and in his discussion of halving, Kūshyār writes of halving amounts which are considered in terms of the

[83] Cantor, *Vorlesungen* (Leipzig, 1894), 1, 674; see Kurt Vogel, *Die Grundlagen der ägyptischen Arithmetik* (Munich, 1929), p. 20; Arnold Buffom Chace, *The Rhind Mathematical Papyrus* (Oberlin, 1927), 1, 3; Neugebauer, *Vorlesungen über Geschichte der antiken mathematischen Wissenschaften*, Vol. 1.

[84] Plato, *Charmides*, 165e.

[85] Benedict, *Comparative Study of Early Treatises*, p. 23.

[86] Arabic text, fol. 274b.

coinage then in use—60 falus being in 1 dirham—so that the need for sexagesimals is obvious.

Unfortunately, too little is understood about the specific methods used by the early Muslims in their sexagesimal calculation. No early Arabic sexagesimal table has yet been found, and not enough is known of these important tables. In ibn Labbān's text there are unfortunate lacunae at this very point: "Thirteenth section on the sexagesimal table and its consequences. The tables of the result of multiplication. Then there are tables of the results of division. Then the sixteenth section is on the simple [i.e. in the decimal system] cube root."[87]

In the text that we have the section immediately following this statement is concerned with cube root extraction. The missing thirteenth section probably included the tables, and the fourteenth and fifteenth sections dealt with their use in multiplication, division, and the resulting powers of the products and quotients.

The only—brief—description of the tables, given in the first section of Book II, states that tables are composed for each of the numbers from 1 to 60, each of the numbers being multiplied sixty times. A table is set down for a number in two rows—in the first the orders of 60 of the multiple, in the second the "parts of 60."[88] Horizontally, across the top, are the "numbers of width," which the tables are "called after." Vertically are the "numbers of length," so that "each of the two [sets of] numbers is made distinct from the other when we mention them."[89] This is followed by an example in which ibn Labbān takes the table to find that "apposite to 25 of the numbers of width and 15 of the numbers of length, is 6 15. The 6 is multiples of 60 when we multiply 25 fifteen times; 15 is the excess and is parts of 60."[90]

In connection with the structure of the table, there is an interesting passage in the section on square root,[91] where the author hunts for the approximate root of 45 degrees: "Then we search in the table for the same numbers of width and length which make 45 or what is close to but less than it. It is necessary that we find this type [of order] in the second row of the table—the first line of it is 0. We find the 6 table apposite another 6 of the numbers of the length gives 0 36. . . ."

Thus, in every one of ibn Labbān's separate tables from 1 to 60 there must have been two top rows. The upper positions are *marātib al-sittīn*, "place positions of 60," and the others *ajzā' al-sittīn*, "parts of 60."

[87] Arabic text, fol. 281a. See E. S. Kennedy and W. R. Transue, "A Medieval Iterative Algorism," *American Mathematical Monthly*, **63**, 80-83 (1956).

[88] This statement is not amplified further, since the tables are missing from the Arabic MS. The exact makeup of ibn Labbān's tables is thus uncertain.

[89] Arabic text, fol. 274b-275a.

[90] Arabic text, fol. 275a.

[91] Arabic text, fol. 278b-279a.

It would appear that Kūshyār wrote the multiplier as he wrote his sexagesimals, in the vertical fashion, each place position above the other, with the higher power of 60 on top. The two rows on top, then, determine the power of the 60 factor in sexagesimals.

Generally, in division, the multiplication tables were used. However, there were also special division tables, as may be seen in the section in Book II on the results of division. Here ibn Labbān speaks of considering the dividend "in the width" and the divisor "in the length." At the meeting place of the numbers consulted, he finds a "2 times" in black. Kūshyār then states that "the numerals in black are raised integers, while those in red are fractions."[92] It was in this manner that the early algorists determined quickly the power of the resulting quotient term.

Sibṭ al-Māradīnī writes of and uses, for greater convenience, twelve tables, instead of the one multiplication table. In the first one, the "numbers of the width" (across) go from 1 to 10, and the "numbers of the length" (vertical) from 1 to 30; the second has 1 to 10 in width and 31 to 60 in length, and so on. The next table goes from 11 to 20, then 21 to 30, etc.

Al-Kāshī uses one table, 1 to 60 in the width, and 1 to 60 in the length, making 3600 squares. He also breaks it up into sixty tables, as does ibn Labbān.

Because of the sexagesimal table, it became simple to convert decimal numbers to sexagesimals. In fact, sexagesimal reckoning itself was much simplified. Division of a smaller number by a larger could be accomplished without difficulty, since the dividend could be multiplied by powers of 60. Later, the power of the result could be read from the special division table. Further, if division was not sufficiently precise, then the remainder was multiplied by 60 and divided again. Ptolemy used this method for finer work.[93]

Incidentally, by means of the tables, conversion of sexagesimals to decimal integers was eased. The process of "raising of numbers," i.e., raising them to higher powers of 60 through division by 60, is well described by ibn Labbān. He does not include sexagesimal to decimal conversion, but he must have known this or he would not have given the cube root process only in decimal numbers. For finding the square root, ibn Labbān used both sexagesimal and decimal procedures, while al-Nasawī and al-Bīrūnī used only the decimal system.

[92] Arabic text, fol. 278b. Unfortunately ibn Labbān and the Arabic mathematicians who followed him could not extend the pregnant idea of the red and black for exponents. It is partly because they continued to use the dust board process rather than adopting a system of writing on a permanent surface.

[93] Heiberg, ed., *Syntaxis mathematica*, 1, 35.

The Concept of "Exponents"[94] in Kūshyār ibn Labbān's Work

Although the Babylonians had worked out a complete system, both fractional and integral, in sexagesimal calculation, the idea of powers in the form of exponents evolved fully only much later. In the development of this concept, ibn Labbān's arithmetic holds an important position. This may be seen in Kūshyār's discussion of the "results of multiplication." He states[95] that the "results of degrees by degrees are degrees, and degrees by fractions are those fractions [for example], as degrees by minutes are minutes, and by seconds are seconds." What is more important is that Kūshyār states, "For fractions by fractions, it is a gathering of the marks as minutes by seconds are thirds, because it is 1 plus 2. Seconds times seconds are fourths, because it is 2 plus 2." The "exponents" are added rhetorically only.

In a similar section,[96] Kūshyār states, under the results of division, that division of degrees by degrees gives degrees, and division of minutes by minutes gives degrees. For degrees divided by fractions give degrees "raised by the number [of marks][97] of the divisor. For example, degrees [divided] by seconds is degrees raised twice; [degrees divided] by fourths is degrees raised four times." By "raising" he means, in this case, multiplying by sixty.[98]

Again, in discussing the division of fractions by degrees, ibn Labbān speaks of it as concerning the "mark of the dividend," and further, when one divides a fraction with a "larger mark" by one with a "smaller," he actually subtracts the mark of the divisor from that of the dividend.[99] Conversely, when one divides a fraction with a smaller mark by one with a larger, he raises the degrees in the answer by the "number between the marks of the dividend and the divisor, as minutes by thirds is a degree raised twice. . . ."[100]

Clearly, ibn Labbān made extensive use of marks, in both multiplication and division. When writing on a permanent surface, he used a

[94] In this discussion, when we place the word "exponents" in quotation marks, we intend it to signify no more than an early concept which developed eventually into what is now known as the exponent. This concept, of necessity, changed from period to period. At times it refers simply to the position of a number-digit. See Tropfke, *Gesch. d. Elem. Math.*, **2**, 132 ff.

[95] Book I, Section 5, Arabic text, fol. 270b.

[96] Book I, Section 7, Arabic text, fols. 271b-272a.

[97] Here, for an exponent which indicates parts of degrees, Kūshyār uses, instead of *lafẓ* another term for "exponent," *ʿadād*.

[98] Arabic text, fol. 272a. See translation.

[99] Arabic text, fol. 272b.

[100] The author speaks—Arabic text (fol. 272b)—of degrees raised twice although he generally works with decimal integrals, and reserves the sexagesimal system for fractional reckoning. This is true again in Book II, Section 6 under multiplication of sexagesimals. See Arabic text, fols. 277a-277b.

system of black and red marks, black for raised integers and red for fractions.[101] In other words, they denoted positive and negative exponents. The colored marks obviously could not have been used on the dust board (had this been possible, improved methods of writing fundamental operations might have developed). But these marks were definitely used on the sexagesimal tables, as we noted earlier.

Kūshyār also used marks in dealing with square roots. In his discussion of the extraction of the square root, he speaks of odd and even "exponents,"[102] and he refers to these again when he takes up the results of square root extraction.[103]

The concept of this kind of mark did not, of course, originate with ibn Labbān. Al-Khwārizmī, in the ninth century, referred to the value of the exponent as the power of 60 in the sexagesimal system.[104] Although Kūshyār used marks extensively, neither he nor other early Islamic mathematicians were aware of negative and zero exponents as such. ʿAnābī writes in his commentary: "In naming degrees in the zero order, the reason is that nothing precedes the degrees, and because the minutes are in the order of the firsts, and the seconds are in the order of the seconds, and so on in this manner."[105]

An understanding of negative and fractional exponents was very slow in evolving, probably for lack of a proper symbolism. Even al-Kāshī, in the fifteenth century, never developed the idea, although he added "exponents" in multiplication and subtracted them in division.[106] It was not until the time of Chuquet (1484) and Stifel (1544) that any substantial understanding of exponents existed.

Kūshyār ibn Labbān and Later Arithmetic

Despite the fact that ibn Labbān's work on arithmetic survives today in only one Arabic manuscript, together with the Hebrew commentary for the first book, there is evidence that Kūshyār exerted a strong influence on later algorists. His student, al-Nasawī,[107] although making

[101] Arabic text, fol. 277a-277b.

[102] Arabic text, fol. 278b. See translation.

[103] Arabic text, fol. 280a.

[104] Boncompagni, ed., *Scritti di Leonardo Pisano*, **1**, 18.

[105] Hebrew text, fol. 44b; not found in the Arabic text.

[106] See Luckey, *Die Rechenkunst*, pp. 56-57. The *Miftāḥ al-ḥisāb* is now in an excellent Russian edition, ed. by Rozenfeld, Segal, and Yushkevich.

[107] See al-Baihaqī, *Tatimma ṣiwān al-ḥikma*, ed. Muḥammad Shafīʿ (Lahore, 1935), **1**, 109-10. "He was a Persian who lived in Raiy and wrote *Al-muqnīʿ fī'l ḥisāb al-hindī*, 'That which is satisfying in Indian reckoning.'" MS Leiden, Rijksuniversiteit, 556 (fols. 68b-79b); Suter, *Bibl. Math.*, Ser. III, **7**, 113-119 (1906); Franz Woepcke, *J. asiat.* **1**, 492-500 (1863).

refinements of his own, still maintained the larger essentials of ibn Labbān's work. In writing of his mathematical debt to his predecessors, al-Nasawī states:

Some have created a type which is related to a kind of practical operation as abū Ḥanīfa al-Dīnawarī and Kūshyār al-Jīlī. In spite of the brief style, Kūshyār wrote an introductory treatise on astronomical reckoning included in practical reckoning, and abū Ḥanīfa wrote an introductory treatise on astronomical calculation, which includes other practical calculation.[108]

Later, in the thirteenth century, Jordanus Nemorarius, an influential algorist, leans heavily, in his *Demonstratio de algorismo*, upon the work of al-Nasawī.[109] As late as the sixteenth century ibn Labbān himself is mentioned by the famous algorist, Sibṭ al-Māradīnī, in the introduction to his *Raqā'iq al-haqā'iq fī ḥisāb al-daraj wa'l-daqā'iq*, "Fine points of the truths of the reckoning of degrees and minutes":

In astronomical calculation, there is nothing more aesthetic than the operations of the sexagesimal system as it is used in our present day when the earlier methods have been given up because of their difficulty and many operations. I have read no satisfactory treatise in this field other than that of . . . Shihābaddīn Aḥmad b. al-Majdī . . . whose title is, "Disclosure of the truths concerning the calculation of degrees and minutes." I do not know of any previous work in this field. In the limits of this science, there are only insignificant, insufficient presentations of Kūshyār and others.[110]

Although Sibṭ refers slightingly to ibn Labbān, it is significant that Kūshyār was still known five hundred years after his death, and that his name was the only one Sibṭ singled out among the early algorists. Furthermore, it is interesting that his treatise on dust board arithmetic was still being used in an era when more permanently written algorismic methods were already very well developed.

The full story of the influence of ibn Labbān on Arabic and medieval European mathematics cannot yet be properly detailed. His other mathematical, and his astronomical, treatises have yet to be edited and published.[111] This fact, together with the lack of editions of Sibt and other important Arab mathematicians, makes a complete analysis of the contributions of ibn Labbān and his successors impossible at this time.

[108] Introduction, MS cited; the translation is by Martin Levey.

[109] See Cantor, *Vorlesungen*, **2**, 85; Baldessarre Boncompagni, *Bibl. Math.*, Ser. III, **5**, 408 (1904); Eneström, *Bibl. Math.*, Ser. III, **7**, 34-37 (1906).

[110] MS Gotha, Herzogliche, 1390 (fol. 1b-2a); see Franz Woepcke, *Sur l'introduction de l'arithmétique indienne en occident* (Rome, 1859), p. 464.

[111] Martin Levey is at present working on a text of ibn Labbān on indeterminate equations.

TEXT
AND
TRANSLATION

KŪSHYĀR IBN LABBĀN

PRINCIPLES OF HINDU RECKONING

In the name of Allah, the Merciful and Compassionate

This book on the principles of Hindu arithmetic is an arrangement of abū al-Ḥasan Kūshyār b. Labbān al-Jīlī, may God have mercy on him.[1] It is comprised of two books, the first is on fundamental principles by the simple, evident, and well-known procedures and the second book is on compound operations by means of a table called the sexagesimal table.[2]

FIRST BOOK

ON THE SIMPLE METHOD

COMPRISING NINE SECTIONS

The purpose in arithmetic is the determination of the unknown quantities mainly through three basic principles. These are multiplication, division, and square root.[3] In multiplication, one of the two numbers is increased as many times as there are units in the other. It is prior to the other two principles, for it is the only way to them. Division is the opposite of multiplication. It is the fragmentation of one of the two numbers into as many parts as there are units in the other. The root is the side of a square. With these there is a fourth principle which is rarely needed and is called the cube root.[4]

Before proceeding with these principles, it is essential to have a knowledge of the symbols of the nine numerals and the place order of [any] one of them with respect to the others and the increase of [any] one [compared] to the others, and the lessening of [any] one of them compared to the others.

---

[1] For the foreword to his Hebrew commentary (fol. 39a), ʿ*Anābī* writes: "Preface of the translator, the sage, R. Shālôm, son of the honorable Rabbi Joseph ʿAnābī, may his Rock and Redeemer keep him, praise and glory to God by contact, not by comparison, for comparison depends upon a representation of the Master of the Earth. The former [contact] is independent of representation and indeed it has no comparison of a representation. Otherwise, all reverts to the second idea. True negation is right and its place is recognized. Praise be to superior men according to the extent of their association with a religious existence. And those close to the superior are approximately the same and the individuals are so. And so praise to the simple according to their souls. And all to the One, One in One, of One who is praised in silence." אמר המעתיק החכם ר׳ שלום בֿכֿר יוסף ענבי יצוֿ השבח והתהלה לאל כפי ההגעה לא כפי ההקפה· כי כל הקפה עמידה על החק מבעל הארץ ואין לראשון הקפה בחק הנה אין לראשון עמידה בחק· והכל ישוב אל התמונה השנית כי השלילה האמתית הוא אשר תצדק ומקומו יכירנו והתהלה לאישי המעלי לפי ההגעה למציאות הדתניי· והקרובים מבעלי המעלה בערך בעלי המעלה ואישיהם כאישיהם וכן התהלה לאישי הפשוטים לפי ערך אישי נפשותם והכל ישוב לאחד אחד באחד מאחד ולו דומיה תהלה·

The Hebrew quotations here are unedited.

[2] ʿAnābī's Hebrew commentary (fol. 39a) also refers to two parts but the second is missing in the only known version: "They consist of two matters which were previously placed in the category of arithmetic according to the Hindus, the first, simple and the second, compound."

بسم الله الرحمن الرحيم
هذا الباب في أصول حساب الهند جمعه أبو الحسن كوشيار
بن لبان الجيلي رحمه الله ويشتمل على مقالتين المقالة الأولى
في استخراج الأصول البسيط الظاهر المعروف والمقالة الثانية
في استخراجها بالمركب ونحو الجدول

المقالة الأولى
في البسط تشتمل على تسعة فصول

الغرض في الحساب وجود كمية المقادير المجهولة والوصول
إلى ذلك على الأمر الأكثر بأصول ثلاثة وهي الضرب
والقسمة والجذر فالضرب تضعيف أحد العددين
بقدر ما في الآخر من الآحاد وله تقدم على ما بعده إذ لا سبيل
إليهما إلا به والقسمة عكس الضرب وهو تجزئة أحد العددين
بقدر ما في الآخر من الآحاد والجذر ضلع المربع وما هنا
أصل رابع يحتاج إليه في العمليات من الأمور يسمى الكعب والذي يجب
أن يتقدم على هذه الأصول معرفة صور الحروف التسعة ورتبة
بعضها عند بعض في الوضع وزيادة بعضها على بعض
ونقصان بعضها من بعض

[3] ʿAnābī's Hebrew commentary (fol. 39a): "He said, 'Here I write what is necessary to establish for the general need. The Hindu arithmetic is according to astronomy and other disciplines in the manner in which the general public uses it, whether according to the discipline as used for whole numbers or whether according to the general public's use in making change, or whatever number it is, or the general public's use of fractions made more precise in studies or in counting change, and for small change until he reaches the division of the numerical remainder, and for the division of the remainder of the remainder until all that is written of our statements comprises twelve chapters.'" אמר הנה אני מחבר מה שצרי׳ לערוך הצורך הכללי וחשבון ההנדיים לפי ערך מלאכת הכוכבים ולפי ערך כלל הלמודיות על דרך ישתמש בה כלל העולם אם לפי הלמודיות כפי השתמש בערך המעלות ואם לפי השתמש כלל העולם בערך הנספר האמר׳ או אי זה מספר היה· והשתמש כלל העולם אל חלקים הדקים בלימודים או נספר הנפרט ואל פריטי הנפרט עד הגיע אל חלוק היתרון המספרי ואל חלוק יתרון היתרון עד יהיה כלל מה שיחובר ממאמרינו זה י״ב שערים·

[4] ʿAnābī's Hebrew commentary (fol. 39a) gives these as value, apportionment, square root, and cube root.

First Section

On the Understanding of the Symbols of the Nine Numerals

These are: ٩٨٧٦٥٤٣٢١. Orders are attributed to these numerals. The first of them is the symbol of the 1. The second is the symbol of the 2 [and so on] until the ninth. Also, the first of them is in the order of the units; the second in the order of the tens; the third [in the order of the] hundreds; the fourth, thousands; the fifth, ten thousands; the sixth, hundred thousands; the seventh, thousand thousands; the eighth, ten thousand thousands; and the ninth, hundred thousand thousands. According to this example the place positions are reckoned. The number of these [numerical symbols in these] place positions is 987,654,321. In the place position where there is no number, a zero is placed as a substitute for that missing number.[5] In the case of the ten a cipher is made to precede it in the place position of the units.[6] Likewise the hundred is preceded by two zeros in the place positions of the units and tens. The other ones are measured according to this analogy. This is the figure for it.

10	ten
100	hundred

Every place position taken within the order of numerals is followed by its tens, then its hundreds, then its thousands. The rest are according to this analogy. Also, every place position taken between other place positions is the tens of what precedes it, the hundreds of what precedes that, and the thousands of what precedes that.[7] For example, a 5 of

---

[5] This is explained in ʿAnābī's Hebrew commentary (fol. 40a): "When he says, 'That among these which have no value . . ., etc.,' he means 'recorded' by the word *neʿelam* because in Arabic *ʿalama* is equivalent to *rōshem*, a sign. It is as if one says no number has an order higher than it, but indeed it stands alone, having no positional value. He means that an order precedes it like the ten alone, the hundred alone, and the thousand alone. We record instead of the missing order a zero." ואומרו ולאשר אין חק מאלו וכו׳· ירצה במלת נעלם נרשום כי הטעם בערבי עלם וכאילו יאמ׳ וכל מספר אין למעלה ממנו מדרגה אבל אמנם הוא לבדו ואין לו ערך מדרגיי ר״ל שנקדם לו מדרגה כמו העשרה לבדם· והק׳ לבדם והאלף לבדם נרשום תחת המדרגה הנפקדת·

[6] It must be remembered that Arabic writing goes from right to left. Therefore, the zero precedes the numeral one in the figure for ten.

[7] A numeral is given its proper place position by the number of numerals which are to the right of it. The decimal point or sexagesimal point notation was not known then.

الفصل الاول في معرفة صور الحروف التسعة
وهي هذه ١ ٢ ٣ ٤ ٥ ٦ ٧ ٨ ٩ ويقال لمحال الحروف
مراتب وللواحد مرتبة والاولى منها علامة الواحد والثانية
علامة الاثنين حتى التاسعة وايضا فان الاولى منها في رتبة
الاحاد والثانية في رتبة العشرات والثالثة مئين
والرابعة الوف والخامسة عشرات الوف والسادسة مئين
الوف والسابعة الوف الوف والثامنة عشرات الوف الوف
والتاسعة مئين الوف الوف وعلى هذا المثال تعد المراتب
فيكون عدد هذه الحروف تسع مائة الف الف وسبعة
وثمانين الف الف وستمائة الف واربعة وخمسين الفا وثلثمائة
واحد وعشرين والمراتب التي لا تكون قبلها عدد يثبت قبل
تلك المرتبة صفر بدلا من ذلك العدد المفقود كالعشرة
تتقدمها صفر بدلا من الاحاد وكالمائة تتقدمها صفران
بدلا من الاحاد والعشرات وعلى هذا القياس نظايرها
وهذه صورة ذلك ١٠ اعني ١٠٠ اماه وكل مرتبة
تفرض فيما بين مراتبها فان التي تليها احاد بعد عشراتها
والتي بعدها مائتها والتي بعدها الوفها وعلى هذا القياس

place-positioned numerals is of the units to a 6, and the 6 is of its tens, and a 7 is of its hundreds, and an 8 of its thousands and so on. Also the 5 is tens to the 4, and it is hundreds to the 3, and it is thousands to the 2, and according to this analogy whatever else is before it.

Second Section

On Addition[8]

We wish to add 839 to 5,625. It is set down according to this first figure.

```
5625
 839        [Fig. 1]
```

The lesser is under the larger and every order is below its corresponding one, units under units, and tens under tens. Then we add the 8 to the 6 which is above it to give 14. We add the 1 of the tens to the 5 to give 6. We put the 4 in place of the 6 and it results in what is in this second figure.

```
6425
 839        [Fig. 2]
```

We add the 3 to the 2 that is above it to give 5. Then we add 9 to 5. This gives rise to 1 ten which we add to the 5 tens, and to 4 units which we put in place of the 5. It results in what is shown in this third figure.

```
6464
 839        [Fig. 3]
```

This is what we wished to do.[9]

---

[8] The general descriptions of the operations for each chapter have been omitted in the extant Arabic copy. ʿAnābī's Hebrew commentary (fol. 40b) has preserved them. For addition, where the given problem is 5627 + 482, one reads: "When you want to do this, set down the augend and under it the addend, every order in the place position proper for it. The units are in the order of the units, the tens in the order of the tens, until whatever number you want. After this we add the last order of the lower line to the corresponding order of the upper line. To that which is before it do likewise until you reach the first order of the lower corresponding to the first order of the upper." כאשר רצית זה הנח המספר הנוסף ותחתיו המספר אשר עליו נוסף כל מדרגה במקום הראוי לה· האחדים במדרגת האחדי והעשרות במדרגת העשרות, עד אי זה מספר רצית· אח״כ נוסיף המדרגה האחרונה מהטור השפל על מדרגת מה שיקביל לה מהטור העליון·

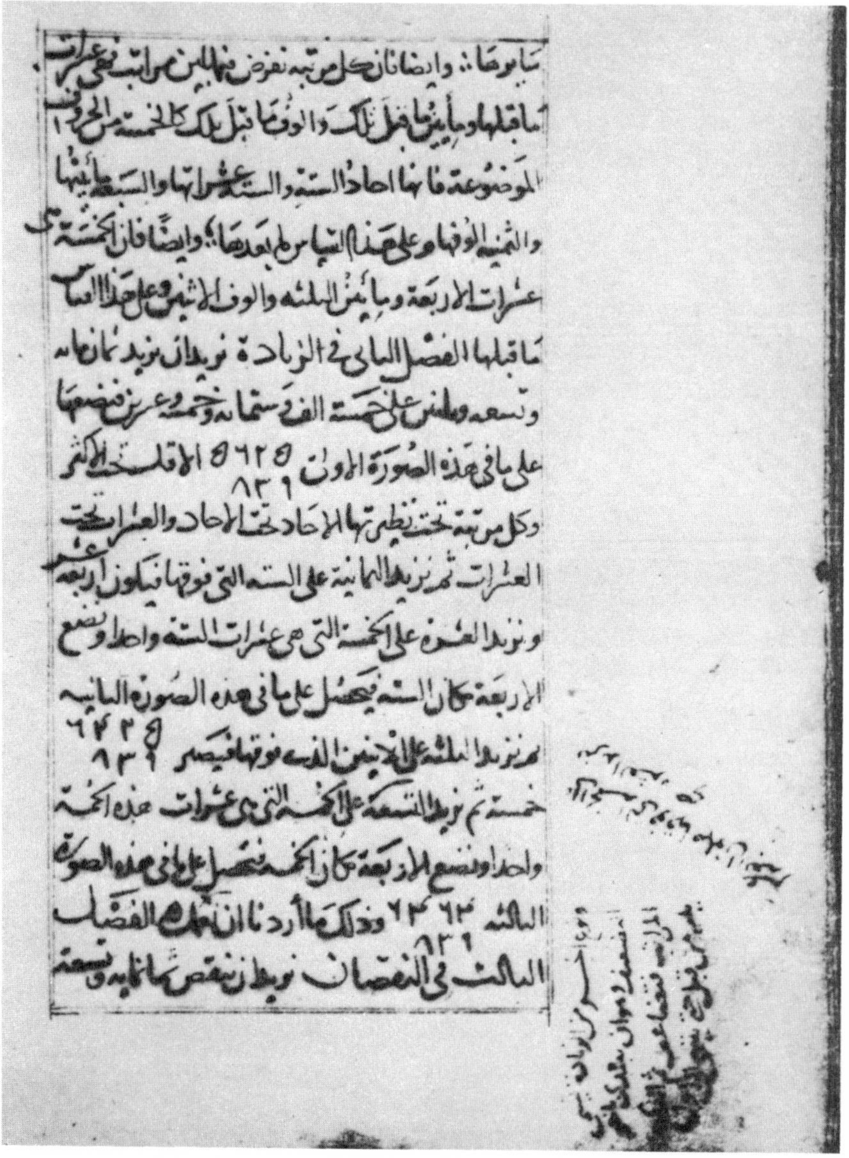

[9] In ʿAnābī's Hebrew commentary (fol. 40b), a further small section on doubling has been preserved: "And one more matter in addition is called doubling (*dōmeh*) and in Arabic *tadʿīf*. You begin with the last order and add it to itself and the same with what is before it to the end." ועוד ענין אחד מהתוספת יקרא דומה בערבי תעדיף והוא שתתחיל ממדרגה האחדים ותוסיפה על דמיונה וכן בשלפניה עד סוף·

Third Section

On Subtraction[10]

We wish to subtract 839 from 5,625. We set it down according to the first figure.

```
5625
 839        [Fig. 1]
```

The smaller one is under the larger one. All of the categories correspond, units under units, tens under tens. Then we subtract the 8 from the 6 which is above it. It is not possible to subtract so we subtract it from the 56 which is above it.[11] There remains 48. We put the 4 in place of the 5 because it is of the order of the tens, and the 8 in place of the 6 because it is of the order of the units. It remains as in the second figure.

```
4825
 839        [Fig. 2]
```

Then we subtract the 3 from the 2 above it. There remains 79. We put the 70 in place of the 80, and the 9 in place of the 2. It remains according to the third figure.

```
4795
 839        [Fig. 3]
```

Then we subtract the 9 from the 5 which is above it. It is impossible to subtract. We subtract it from 95 which is above it. There remains 86. We put the 80 in place of the 90 and the 6 in place of the 5. It remains according to the fourth figure.

```
4786
 839        [Fig. 4]
```

That is what we wished to do.

---

[10] The general description in ʻAnābī's Hebrew commentary (fol. 41b) goes: "Now we set down first the desired minuend and under it the subtrahend, each order apposite to each order, units under units, tens under tens, and hundreds under hundreds. Then subtract the last order of the lower line from the upper order corresponding to it and then that beside it corresponding to it from the upper until you reach the first of the lower. Subtract it from that which corresponds to it in the upper."-הנה נניח ראשונה הערך אשר נרצה לחסר ותחתיו מה שממנו נחסר על מדרגה נגד מדרגה זו תחת זו העשרו׳ תחת העשרות והמאות תחת המאות· אח״כ חסר המדרגה האחרונה מהטור השפל ממדרגה הנקבלת לה מהעליון, ואשר בצדה מהנקבלת לה מהעליון עד שתגיע אל הראשונה מהשפל לחסרה מהנקבלת לה מהעליון· וכל מדרגה אשר לא תספיק לחסר ממנו נחסר ממדרגה שלפניה אחד ונפזרנו לי·

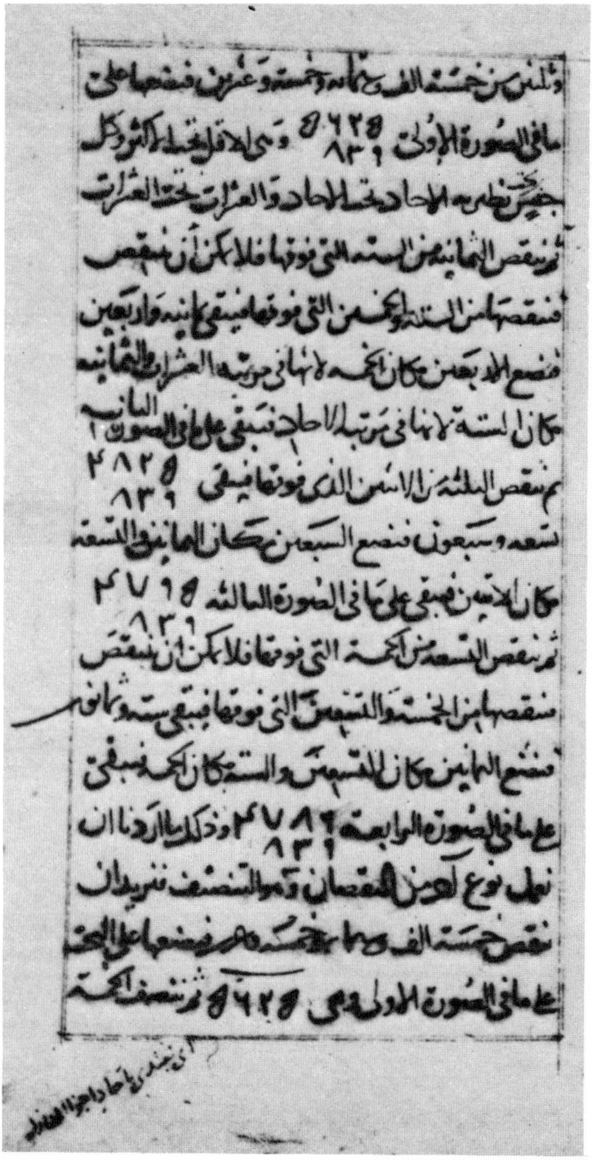
وثلثين من خمسة الف وستمائة وخمسة وعشرين فنضعها على
ما في الصورة الاولى ٥٦٢٥ / ٨٣٩ وهي الاقل تحت الاكثر وكل
جنس نظيره الاحاد تحت الاحاد والعشرات تحت العشرات
ثم ننقص الثمانية من الستة التي فوقها فلا يمكن ان ننقص
فننقصها من الستة والخمسين التي فوقها فيبقى ثمانية واربعين
فنضع الاربعين مكان الخمسة لانها في مرتبة العشرات والثمانية
مكان الستة لانها في مرتبة الاحاد فيبقى على ما في الصورة الثانية
٤٨٢٥ / ٨٣٩ ثم ننقص الثلثة من الاثنين الذي فوقها فيبقى
تسعة وسبعون فنضع السبعين مكان الثمانية والتسعة
مكان الاثنين فيبقى على ما في الصورة الثالثة ٤٧٩٥ / ٨٣٩
ثم ننقص التسعة من الخمسة التي فوقها فلا يمكن ان ننقص
ننقصها من الخمسة والتسعين التي فوقها فيبقى ستة وثمانون
فنضع الثمانين مكان التسعين والستة مكان الخمسة فيبقى
على ما في الصورة الرابعة ٤٧٨٦ / ٨٣٩ وذلك ما اردنا ان
نعمل نوع آخر من النقصان وهو التنصيف نريد ان
ننصف خمسة الف وستمائة وخمسة وعشرين فنضعها على
على ما في الصورة الاولى وهي ٥٦٢٥ ثم ننصف الخمسة

[11] ʿAnābī's Hebrew commentary (fol. 41b) performs this operation in a more modern manner: "For every order which is insufficient to be subtracted from, we subtract 1 from the order before it and we convert it to 10."

Another kind of Subtraction, Which is Halving[12]

We wish to halve 5,625.[13] We set it down according to the figure.

5625 [*Fig. 1*]

We halve the first 5 of the number to get 2 $\frac{1}{2}$. We put the 2 in place of the 5 and put the $\frac{1}{2}$ under it, 30.

5622
30 [*Fig. 2*]

If it is considered a dirham, they are the falus. If it is used as a degree, they are minutes. We halve the 2 in the tens; 1 remains in its place. We halve the 6 after it; a 3 remains in its place according to the third figure.

5312
30 [*Fig. 3*]

Then we halve the last 5 which is tens of the 3 preceding it. Its half is 25. We put the 20 in place of the 5 because it is the order of the tens in relation to the 3. We add the 5 to the 3 which is from its units. There remains what is according to the fourth figure.

2812
30 [*Fig. 4*]

Fourth Section

On Multiplication[14]

We wish to multiply 325 by 243. The two are placed on the dust board as in the first figure.

---

[12] The general process in ʿAnābī's Hebrew commentary (fol. 41b) is given as: "He says, 'Halving in Arabic is *tanṣīf*.' It is that you begin with the first order of the row and halve it. If half comes out to $\frac{1}{2}$, place 30 under it for it is $\frac{1}{2}$ of 60. Further, divide every order which is before this order. . . ." ונקרא החסייא בערבי תנציף· והוא שתתחיל ממדרגה הראשונה מהטור מחציה· ואם נזדמן חצי בחציה שים תחתיו ל והוא חצי הששים, הא· גם חלק כל מדרגה אשר לפני·

[13] ʿAnābī's Hebrew commentary (fol. 42a) begins with 5624.

[14] ʿAnābī's Hebrew translation gives a very brief description of multiplication. It is obviously from a much more abbreviated Arabic version. His commentary (fol 42b) is

المرتبة التي هي الاحاد فيكون اثنان ونصف فنسقط
كان الخمسة ونضع النصف تحتها الثلثين على ما في الصورة الثانية
٥٦٢٢
٣٠
ان استعملنا الدرهم كان فلوس وان استعملت في
الدرج كان دقايق ثم ننصف الاثنين الذي هو العشرات
فيبقى مكانه واحد ثم ننصف الستة التي بعده فيبقى مكانها
ثلثة على ما في الصورة الثالثة ٥٣١٢ ثم ننصف الخمسة
٣٠
الاخيرة فلانها عشرات الثلثة التي قبلها يكون نصفها خمسة
وعشرين فنضع العشرين مكان الخمسة لانها بمرتبة العشرات
بالاضافة الى الثلثة ونزيد الخمسة على الثلثة التي هي احادها
فيصير ثمانية ونبقى على ما في الصورة الرابعة ٢٨١٢
٣٠
الفصل الرابع في الضرب نريد ان نضرب ثلثمائة
وخمسة وعشرين في ماتين وثلثة واربعين فنضعهما على التخت
على ما في الصورة الاولى ٣٢٥ اول المراتب السفلانية
٢٤٣
تحت اخر مراتب الفوقانية ابدا ثم نضرب الثلثة الفوقانية
في الاثنين السفلاني فيكون ستة فنضعها فوق الاثنين
السفلاني بازاء الثلثة الفوقانية على ما في الصورة الثانية
٦٣٢٥ فلو كانت الستة عشرات كنا نضعها بعد الستة
٢٤٣

'Put down the multiplicand and under it its multiplier, the first order
e last order of the upper. Commence with the last order of the
ltiply it by the last order of the lower line and do likewise
re it until we have multiplied the last order of the upper by
er. Place the result apposite every order equally. Then you shift
er orders to the right side of the number and multiply by that
upper by each one of the lower orders. The beginning of multipli-
ne at first. There should not remain any multiplier order that you
other, until the end of the multiplication of the first order of the
lower. Whatever is added together of all of the [results of the]
l of the multiplication." שים המספר המוכה ותחתיו אשר בו תכה

325
243 [*Fig. 1*]

The first order of the multiplier is under the last place position of the multiplicand. Multiply the 3 of the multiplicand by the 2 of the multiplier to give 6. We put it above the 2 of the multiplier beside the 3 of the multiplicand according to the second figure.

6 325
243 [*Fig. 2*]

If the product were other than 6 and contained tens and units, we would have put the units above the 2 and the tens to the left of the units. We multiply the upper 3 also by the lower 4. We add the 10 to the tens so that 6 becomes 7. It results in what is in the third figure.

72325
243 [*Fig. 3*]

We multiply the upper 3[15] by the lower 3 to give 9. We put it above the lower 3 in place of the upper 3. We shift the lower orders one place [to the right]. It results in what is shown in the fourth figure.

72925
 243 [*Fig. 4*]

Then we multiply the 2 which is above the lower 3 by the lower 2 to get 4. We add it to the 2 that is above the lower 2 to get 6. Then we multiply the upper 2 by the lower 4 to get 8. We add it to the 9 which is above the 4. Then we multiply the upper 2 also by the lower 3 to get 6. We put it above the 3 in place of the upper 2. Then we shift the lower orders one place [to the right]. It results in what is shown in the fifth figure.[16]

77765
  243 [*Fig. 5*]

Then we multiply the upper 5 by the lower 2 to give 10. We add it to the tens order [of] that [which] is above the 4. Again, we multiply the 5 by

---

המדרגה הראשונה מהשפל תחת המדרגה האחרונה מהעליון· ותתחיל מהמדרגה האחרונה לטור העליון· ונכה עם המדרגה האחרונה של הטור השפל ועשה כן גם במדרג׳ שלפניה עד שנכה המדרגה האחרונה מהעליון עם כל מדרגה מהשפל· ושים העולה כנגד על כל מדרגה בשוה·· עוד תעתיק המדרגה ההיא

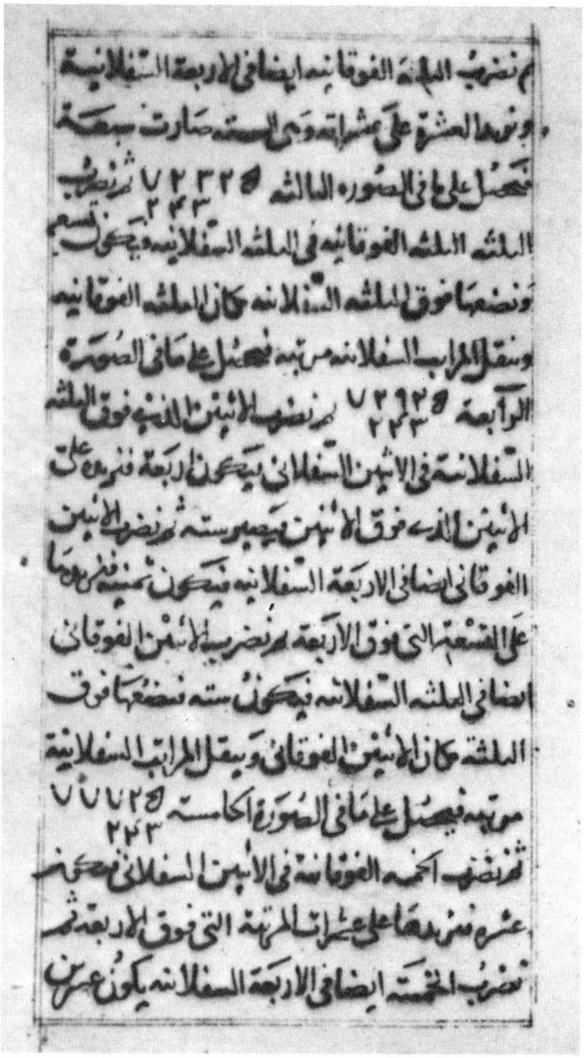

ثم نضرب الثلثة الفوقانيه ايضا في الاربعة السفلانية
ونزيدها العشرة على عشراتها وهي الستة صارت سبعة
فيحصل على ما في الصورة الثالثة ٧٢٣٣٥ ثم نضرب
٢٣٣
الثلثة الفوقانية في الثلثة السفلانية فيكون تسعه
ونضعها فوق الثلثة لانه كان الثلثة الفوقانيه
ونقل المراتب السفلانية مرتبه فيحصل على ما في الصورة
الرابعة ٧٢٩٣٥ ثم نضرب الاثنين اللذين فوق الثلثة
٢٣٣
السفلانية في الاثنين السفلاني فيكون اربعة فنزيدها على
الاثنين الذي فوق الاثنين فيصير ستة ثم نضرب الاثنين
الفوقاني ايضا في الاربعة السفلانية فيكون ثمنية فنزيدها
على التسعة التي فوق الاربعة ثم نضرب الاثنين الفوقاني
ايضا في الثلثة السفلانية فيكون ستة نضعها فوق
الثلثة مكان الاثنين الفوقاني ونقل المراتب السفلانية
مرتبه فيحصل على ما في الصورة الخامسة ٧٧٦٢٥
٢٣٣
ثم نضرب الخمسة الفوقانية في الاثنين السفلاني فيكون
عشرة فنزيدها على عشرات المرتبة التي فوق الاربعة ثم
نضرب الخمسة ايضا في الاربعة السفلانية يكون عشرين

מהמדרגות השפלות על צד ימין המספר ונכה שעל המדרגה הראשונה מהשפל עם כל א' מהמדרגות השפל. ותחילת ההכאה כמו שעשית ראשונה ואל ישאר שלא תעתיק כל המדרגה המוכה זו אחר זו עד סוף הכות המדרגה הראשונה מהעליון עם מדרגה מהשפל ויהיה מה שיקובץ מכל המדרגות השפל הוא המחובר מההכאה..

[15] The "3" is repeated in the Arabic text, presumably a scribal error.

[16] The Arabic text has a two (٢) instead of a six (٦). ʿAnābī's Hebrew commentary has the correct numerals.

the lower 4 to give 20. We add the 2 to the tens order [of that which is above it] to give 9. Again, we multiply the 5 by the lower 3 to give 15; the 5 is left in its place and the 10 is added to its tens. It results in what is shown in the sixth figure.

78975	
243	[*Fig. 6*]

That is what we wished to do.

Multiplication of Degrees and Fractions

If we wish to multiply degrees with fractions [by degrees with fractions], we convert the degrees with fractions, of the two numbers, to the category of the lowest fraction in each of them. Thus, we multiply the degrees by 60 and add the minutes to it. We also multiply the result by 60 and add it to the seconds, and so on with what follows. Then we multiply the derived fraction of one by the derived fraction of the other.

Fifth Section

On the Results of Multiplication

The results of multiplication of degrees by degrees are degrees, and degrees by fractions are those fractions [for example], as degrees by minutes are minutes, and by seconds are seconds. For fractions by fractions, it is a gathering of the marks as minutes by seconds are thirds because it is 1 plus 2.[17] Seconds times seconds are fourths because it is 2 plus 2.[18]

---

[17] ʻAnābī does not write of the "mark," or "exponent," in his commentary but his rules are obvious in showing their addition for multiplication. The Arabic text, however, is more definite.

[18] The exponents are added rhetorically for

$$\frac{x}{60} \cdot \frac{y}{60^2} = \frac{xy}{60^3}$$

and

$$\frac{a}{60^2} \cdot \frac{b}{60^2} = \frac{ab}{60^4}$$

because it is 2 plus 2.

فنزيد على عشرات الاربعة فيصير تسعة ثم نضرب ايضا الخمسة
فى الثلثة السفلانية يكون خمسة عشر فنترك الخمسة مكانها
ونزيد العشرة على عشراتها فتحصل عندنا فى الصورة السادسة ١
٧ ٨٦٧٥ وذلك ما اردنا ان نعمل ضرب الدرج والكسور
٢٤٣
فان اردنا ضرب درج وكسور نقلنا الدرج والكسور
من كل واحد منهما الى جنس الكسر الاخير الذى معه
وهو ان نضرب الدرج فى ستين ونزيد عليه الدقايق التى
معه ونضرب المبلغ ايضا فى ستين ونزيد عليه الثوانى وعلى
هذا ما تبعه ثم نضرب الكسور الحاصلة من احدهما
فى الكسور الحاصلة من الآخر الفصل الخامس
فى الحاصل من الضرب الحاصل من ضرب الدرج فى
الدرج درج والدرج فى الكسور ذلك الكسور كالدرج فى
الدقايق دقايق وفى الثوانى ثوانى ومن الكسور فى الكسور
مجموع اللفظين كالدقايق فى الثوانى ثوالث لانه
واحد واثنين والثوانى فى الثوانى روابع لانه اثنين واثنين والله اعلم
الفصل السادس فى القسمة نريد ان نقسم خمسة الف
وستمائة وخمسة وعشرين على مايتين وثلثة واربعين فنضعها

Sixth Section

On Division[19]

We wish to divide 5,625 by 243. We set it down according to the first figure.

5625
243 [*Fig. 1*]

The last of the orders of the divisor is under the last of the orders of the dividend and that next to it under that next to it. Then a number is sought which we multiply by the lower 2 and then by every one of the orders with it. It is subtracted from the orders which are above it. Its being wiped out [by coming to an answer of 0] completes it or there is a remainder less than the divisor. It is found to be 2 which is set down above that under which is the first of the lower orders according to the second figure.

2
5625 [*Fig. 2*]
243

We multiply it by the lowest 2 to get 4 which is subtracted from the 5 that is above the lowest 2. Also, we multiply it by the lower 4 and subtract it from what is above the 4. Again, we multiply by the lower 3 and subtract it from what is above the 3. Then we shift the lower orders one place.[20] It is according to what is in the third figure.

2
765 [*Fig. 3*]
243

Then we seek a number which if we multiply it by the lower 2 [and] by every one of the orders with it, and we subtract it from the orders above it, it all comes out to nothing or there is a remainder which is

[19] The general description of division in ʿAnābī's Hebrew commentary (fol. 44b), where the given problem is 5627 ÷ 243—the difference being acknowledged by ʿAnābī (fol. 46b), is given as follows: "We set down the dividend and under it the divisor, the last order of the lower under the last order of the dividend. Further, place the sought number [partial quotient] above the first order of the lower. Then we seek a number with which we multiply every order of the lower and begin herein with the last order of the lower. We subtract the result of every one of those multiplied from the orders of the dividend. Further, we shift an order of the lower to the right of the number and we put the first of the lower, the sought one, on the order which is under it. We carry on by the

[FOLIO 271a]

على ما في الصورة الاولى ٥٦٢٥ الاخير من مراتب
٢٤٣
المقسوم عليه تحت الاخير من مراتب المقسوم وما يليه
تحت الذي يليه ثم نطلب عددًا ان ضربناه في الاثنين
السفلاني ثم في كل واحد مما معه من المراتب ونقص من
المراتب التي فوقها افناها كلها او بقي منها ما هو اقل من المقسوم
عليه فنجده اثنين فنضعه فوق التي تحتها اول المراتب
٢
السفلانية على ما في الصورة الثانية ٥٦٢٥ ونضربه
٢٤٣
في الاثنين السفلاني فيكون اربعة فننقصه من الخمسة
التي فوق الاثنين السفلاني ونضربه ايضا في الاربعة
السفلانية وننقصه مما فوق الاربعة ونضربه ايضا في
الثلثة السفلانية وننقصه مما فوق الثلثة وننقل المراتب
السفلانية مرتبة فتكون على ما في الصورة الثالثة
٧٦٥
ثم نطلب عددًا اذا ضربناه في الاثنين السفلانية ٢٤٣
في كل واحد مما معه من المراتب ونقصناه من المراتب
التي فوقها افناها كلها او بقي منها ما هو اقل من المقسوم
عليه فنجده ثلثة فنضعها فوق المرتبة التي تحتها اول
المراتب السفلانية فيقع بجنب الاثنين الموضوع اولًا

first plan until the quotient reaches the first order of the upper, the dividend. The amount is the quotient and the remainder of the dividend is fractions of the lower, whatever they are." נשים המספר הנרצה לחלוק ותחתיו המספר אשר בו נחלקהו סוף המדרגה האחרונה מהשפל תחת המדרגה האחרונה מהמספר הנרצה לחלוק· עוד שים המבוקש על המדרגה הראשונה מהשפל· אחר נבקש מספר נכה בו כל מדרגה מהשפל ויתחיל בזה מהמדרגה האחרונה לשפל ונחסר העולה מכל א׳ מהמוכים ממדרגות המספר הנרצה לחלוק· עוד תעתיק מדרגה מהשפל אל ימין המספר ונשים על המדרגה אשר תחתיה הראשונה מהשפל המספר המבוקש ונעשה בו כמשפט הראשון עד שיגיע המבוקש אל המדרגה הראשונה מהעליון אשר הוא המספר הנרצה לחלוק והמחובר הוא חלוק המספר הנרצה והנשאר מהמספר הנרצה הוא חלקי׳ מהמספר השפל מאי זה א׳ מהם·

[20] ʿAnābī's Hebrew commentary (fol. 46b) reads, "The pith of the matter is the placing of the three figures, the first according to the first division, the second according to the

less than the [partial] dividend. We find it is 3. We put it above the order under which is the first of the lower orders, and it is left at the side of the 2 which was placed first according to the fourth figure.

23	
765	[*Fig. 4*]
243	

We multiply the upper found 3 by the lower 2, then subtract it from what is above the 2. We multiply it by the lower 4 and subtract it from what is above the 4. Also, we multiply it by the lower 3 and subtract it from what is above it. It is shown in the fifth figure.

23	
36	[*Fig. 5*]
243	

The result of this division is 23 and 36 parts of 243 [parts] of 1. If the remainder is multiplied by 60 and divided by 243, then it is made in terms of falus of a dirham or as minutes of a degree. Then if the remainder is again multiplied by 60 and divided by what we mentioned, the sixtieths of the falus of the dirham result or seconds of a degree. That is what we wish to do.

Division of the Integer with a Fraction by Another

If we wish, we change the integers which have fractions with them, every one of them to the category of the lowest fraction as was mentioned previously in multiplication. Then the fractions are divided by fractions.[21]

first shift made, and the third according to the second shift." והנ הניח ג צורות הא כנגד החלוקה הראשונה· והב כנגד ההעתקה הראשונה שעשה· והב כנגד ההעתקה הב שעשה·

[21] At this point, ʿAnābī discusses pure sexagesimal division. See Hebrew commentary (fol. 47a). A sexagesimal table is not mentioned and the discussion is very brief.

٣ ٢

على ما في الصورة الرابعة يح ٦ ٧ ونضربها على الثلثة

٣ ٤ ٢

الموجودة في الايمن السفلاني وننقصه مما فوق الايمن

ونضربها ايضا في الاربعة السفلانية وننقصه مما فوق

الاربعة ونضربها ايضا في الثلثة السفلانية وننقصه مما

٤ ٢

فوقها فنحصل على ما في الصورة الخامسة ٦ ٣ فالحاصل

٣ ٤ ٢

من جهة القسمة ثلثة عشر من جزء وستة وثلثون من مايتين

وثلثة واربعين من واحد فاذا ضرب الباقي في ستين

وقسم على مايتين وثلثة واربعين حصل فلوس من درهم

او دقايق من درجة ثم ان ضرب الباقي ايضا في ستين

وقسم على ما ذكرناه حصل فلوس الفلوس من درهم او ثواني

من درجة وذلك ما اردنا ان نعمل قسمة الصحاح

والكسور بعضها على بعض اذا اردنا ذلك نقلنا

الصحاح والكسور التي معها من كل واحد منهما الى جنس

الكسر الاخر كما تقدم ذكره في الضرب ثم نقسم الكسور

على الكسور الفصل السابع في الحاصل من القسمة

وذلك على خمسة اوجه ا الدرج على الدرج ب والدرج

على الكسور ج والكسور على الدرج د والكسور على الكسور

Seventh Section

On the Results of Division[22]

This is according to five types: (1) degrees by degrees, (2) degrees by fractions, (3) fractions by degrees, (4) fractions with a larger mark by those with a smaller one, (5) fractions with a smaller mark by those with a larger one.

Section on results of division of degrees by degrees being degrees; similarly, the fraction by its similar one, as minutes [divided] by minutes being degrees; also seconds by seconds being degrees.

Section on the division of degrees by fractions being degrees raised by the number [of marks] of the divisor. For example, degrees [divided] by seconds is degrees raised twice, [degrees divided] by fourths is degrees raised four times. By "raised,"[23] I mean that the quotient must be multiplied by 60 and that this product must be multiplied by 60. The final product will then give the answer of the division of degrees by seconds. Or we multiply by 60 four times to give the result of the division of degrees by fourths.

Example: If we divide 10 degrees by 5 seconds, the result of the division is 2. We multiply it by 60 and this answer by 60 to get 7,200. It is the result of the division of 10 degrees by 5 seconds. Again we divide 10 degrees by 5 fourths to give 2. Then we multiply it by 60 four times to get 25,920,000 to give the result of the division of 10 degrees by 5 fourths.

As a simpler alternative, we may do this: The result of the division of degrees by degrees is degrees, and similarly the fraction by its kind, as minutes by minutes is degrees, and seconds by seconds is degrees. As to the changing of the fractions, we convert them [both divisor and dividend] into the category of the smaller fraction of the two. Then we divide the like by the like to get the answer in degrees.

Section on the results of the division of fractions by degrees which concerns the mark of the dividend, as seconds [divided] by degrees is seconds, and fourths by degrees is fourths.

Section on the division of a fraction with a larger mark by one with a smaller mark. The mark of the dividend is lessened by the mark of the divisor as thirds by minutes is seconds, and fourths by minutes is thirds.[24]

---

[22] I.e. determination of the powers of terms in the quotient.

[23] ʿAnābī states in his Hebrew commentary (fol. 47a), that raising is when "units are raised or reduced to different units." Later on, he writes that it is only in the case of elevation to higher units.

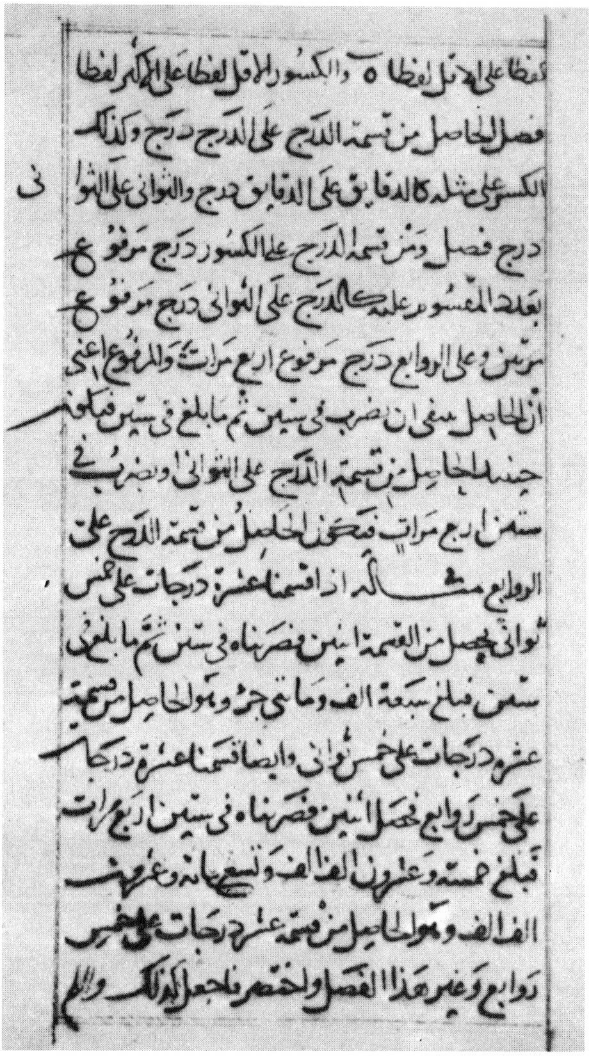

لفظا على الاقل لفظا ه والكسور الاقل لفظا على الاكثر لفظا
فصل الحاصل من قسمة الدرج على الدرج درج وكذلك
الكسور على مثله كالدقايق على الدقايق درج والثواني على الثوا ني
درج فصل ومن قسمة الدرج على الكسور درج مرفوع
بعدد المقسوم عليه كالدرج على الثواني درج مرفوع
مرتين وعلى الروابع درج مرفوع اربع مرات والمرفوع اعني
ان الحاصل ينبغي ان ضرب في ستين ثم ما بلغ في ستين فيكون
جنسه الحاصل من قسمة الدرج على الثواني او ضرب في
ستين اربع مرات فيحصل الحاصل من قسمة الدرج على
الروابع مثاله اذا قسمنا عشرة درجات على خمس
ثواني يحصل من القسمة اثنين فضربناه في ستين ثم ما بلغ في
ستين فبلغ سبعة الف ومايتي جزء وهو الحاصل من قسمة
عشرة درجات على خمس ثواني وايضا قسمنا عشرة درجات
على خمس روابع يحصل اثنين فضربناه في ستين اربع مرات
فبلغ خمسة وعشرون الف الف وتسعمائة وعشرين
الف الف وهو الحاصل من قسمة عشرة درجات على خمس
روابع وعلى هذا الفصل واختصر ما جعل لذلك والله

---

24 $$\frac{x}{60^3} \div \frac{y}{60} = \frac{x}{60^3} \cdot \frac{60}{y} = \frac{x}{y} \cdot 60^{-2} = \frac{x}{y} \text{ seconds,}$$

$$\frac{x}{60^4} \div \frac{y}{60} = \frac{x}{60^4} \cdot \frac{60}{y} = \frac{x}{y} \cdot 60^{-3} = \frac{x}{y} \text{ thirds.}$$

Section on the division of a fraction with a smaller mark by one with a larger one. The degree is raised by the number between the marks of the dividend and divisor, as minutes by thirds is a degree raised twice, and thirds by fourths is a degree raised once.[25]

Eighth Section

On Square Root[26]

We wish to extract the root of a square whose number is 65,342. We set it down on the dust board and differentiate the place positions by means of marking off the digits in twos [from the right] until the

---

25

$$\frac{x \cdot 60^{-1}}{y \cdot 60^{-3}} = \frac{x}{y} \cdot 60^{2}$$

$$\frac{x \cdot 60^{-3}}{y \cdot 60^{-4}} = \frac{x}{y} \cdot 60$$

26 The generalized method is found in ʿAnābī's Hebrew commentary (fol. 48b). "Set down the number whose root is wanted and [from the right] mark off the digits by twos, in Arabic *munṭaq* and *aṣamm*, until you reach the last marked one. Then we seek the sought number. We multiply it by itself and we subtract it from the considered number. The remainder is the wanted number. Then place the sought number under the last marked digit and above it. We multiply what is above it by what is below it and we subtract it from the wanted number. Then we double the lower in its place. We shift it from its order to the right of the number supplied. Then we seek another sought number. We multiply it by the lower order and by itself and subtract it from the number. This remainder is the number. Then place this number on the side of the lower and apposite above. We multiply this carried one by every one of the lower order; we subtract the result from the number. Then we double the lower in its place and shift the lower order from its order. Then we seek the sought number like the first and we do as we did until the sought number falls under the first order and above it. Then we always add 1 and the upper order is the root. The remainder of the root is apposite each one of the lower orders."

שים המספר נרצה השרש ומנה המדרגות המדברות והאלמות· בערבי מנט״ך ואסא עד הגיעך למדברת האחרונה· אחר נבקש המספר המבוקש ונכהו בנפשו ונגרעהו מהמספר הנרצה ונשאר הוא המספר הנרצה· אחר שים המבוקש תחת המדברת האחרונה ועליה ונכה מה שעליה עם מה שתחתיה ונשליכהו מהמספר הנרצה· אחר נכפול השפל במקומו· ואחר נעתיקהו ממדרגתו אל ימין המספר הנתקן· אחר נבקש עוד מבוקש אחר ונכהו עם המדרגה השפל ובנפשו והשליכהו מהמספר הנרצה והנשאר הוא המספר· אחר שים זה המספר בצד מהשפל וכנגדו למעלה ונכה זה הנשאר עם כל א׳ ממדרגות השפל והיוצא השליכהו מהמספר· אחר תכפול השפל במקומו אחר תעתיק המדרגה השפלה ממדרגתה· אחר נבקש מבוקש כאשר בראשונה ונעשה כמו שעשינו עד שיפול המבוקש תחת המדרגה הראשונה ועליה ונעשה זה המעשה עליו· אחר נוסיף עליו א׳ לעולם ותהיה המדרגה העליונה השרש· ויתרון השרש נגד כל א׳ סהמדרגו׳ השפלים·

See page 11 of the Introduction for a discussion of the Arabic words *munṭaq* and *aṣamm* and their Hebrew equivalents.

الحاصل من قسمة الدرج على الدرج درج وكذلك الكسر على
مثله كالدقايق على الدقايق درج والثوان على الثواني
درج وما اختلف من الكسور نقلناهما الى جنس ادونهما
كما ذكرنا فيما المثل على المثل يحصل الدرج فصل والحاصل
من قسمة الكسور على الدرج لفظ المقسوم كالثواني
على الدرج ثواني والروابع على الدرج روابع فصل
ومن قسمة الكسر الاكثر لفظا على الاقل لفظا لفظ المقسوم
منقوص منه لفظ المقسوم عليه كالثوالث على الدقايق
ثواني والروابع الدقايق ثوالث فصل ومن قسمة الكسر
الاقل لفظا على الاكثر لفظا درج مرفوع بعدد ما بين لفظ
المقسوم والمقسوم عليه كالدقايق على الثوالث درج
مرفوع مرتين والثوالث على الروابع درج مرفوع مرة فليعلم
الفصل الثامن في الجذر مثاله نستخرج جذر مال
عدده خمسة وستون الفا وثلثمائة واثنان واربعون
نضعها على التخت ثم نعد المراتب بمنطق واصم الى
ان ننتهي الى المنطق الاخير فنضع عددا اذا ضربناه في
نفسه ونقصناه مما فوقه من المال افناه او بقي ما هو اقل

last mark is reached. A number is set down. It is such that if we multiply it by itself and subtract it from what is above it of the square, it comes to zero or there remains what is less than the found squared number. We find it to be 2. We put it under the 6 and above it also as in the first figure.

2
65342 [*Fig. 1*]
2

Then we square it and subtract it from what is above it of the square. We double the 2 in its place and shift it and the upper 2 one place to that shown in the second figure.

2
25342 [*Fig. 2*]
4

Then we seek a number which we put under the 3 such that if we multiply it by the lower 4, then by itself, and we subtract it from what is above it of the square, it comes to 0 or the remainder is less than the lower orders. It is 5 which we put under the 3 and also above it as in the third figure.

25
25342 [*Fig. 3*]
45

Then we multiply it [the 45] by 5 and subtract it from what is above it of the square. Then we double the 5 in its place and shift the lower and upper orders one place as in the fourth figure.

25
2842 [*Fig. 4*]
50

Then we seek a number which if we multiply it by the lower orders, then by itself, and we subtract it from what is above it of the square, either nothing is left or the remainder is less than the lower orders. It is a 5 which we put under the 2 and above it. We multiply it by the 5 and subtract it from what is above the 5 of the square and we multiply it by

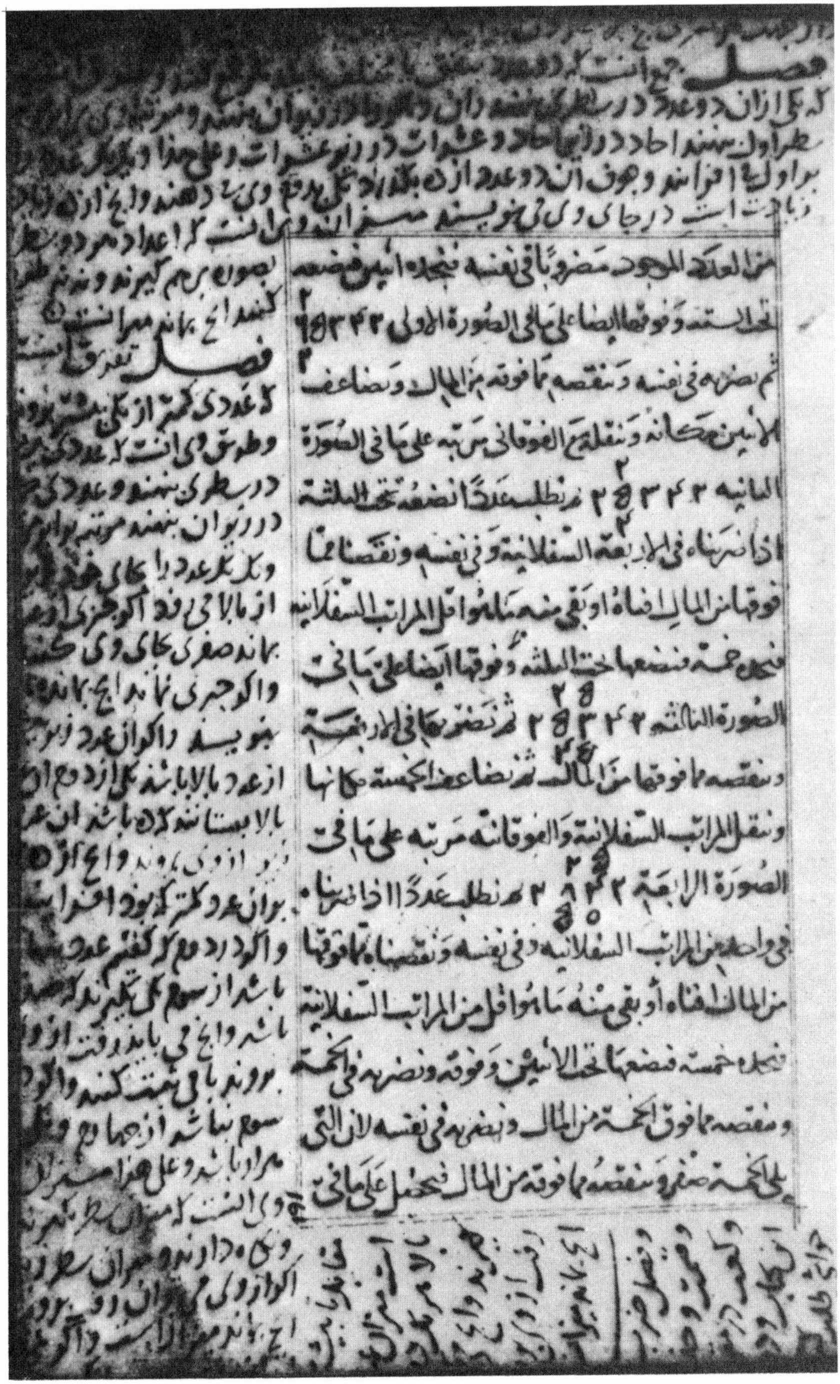

من العدد الموجود مضروبًا في نفسه فنجده اثنين فنضعه
تحت الستة وفوقها ايضا على ما في الصورة الاولى ٢ ٤ ٣ ٣ ٤ ٦
ثم نضربه في نفسه وننقصه مما فوقه من المال ونضاعف
الاثنين مكانه وننقلهما الفوقاني مرتبة على ما في الصورة
الثانية ٢ ٤ ٣ ٣ ٦ ٢ ثم نطلب عددًا نضعه تحت الثلثة
اذا ضربناه في الاربعة السفلانية وفي نفسه ونقصنا مما
فوقها من المال افناه او بقي منه ما هو اقل من المراتب السفلانية
فنجده خمسة فنضعها تحت الثلثة وفوقها ايضا على ما في
الصورة الثالثة ٢ ٤ ٣ ٣ ٦ ٢ ثم نضربها في الاربعة
وننقصه مما فوقها من المال ثم نضاعف الخمسة مكانها
وننقل المراتب السفلانية والفوقانية مرتبة على ما في
الصورة الرابعة ٢ ٤ ٣ ٩ ٢ ثم نطلب عددًا اذا ضربناه
في واحد من المراتب السفلانية وفي نفسه ونقصناه مما فوقها
من المال افناه او بقي منه ما هو اقل من المراتب السفلانية
فنجده خمسة فنضعها تحت الاثنين وفوقه ونضربه في الخمسة
وننقصه مما فوق الخمسة من المال ونضربه في نفسه لان التي
تحت الخمسة صفر وننقصه مما فوقه من المال فنحصل على ما في

itself because that next to the 5 is a 0. We subtract it from what is above it of the square to give the result shown in the fifth figure.

255
317 [*Fig. 5*]
511

The uppermost orders give the root of the square. The remainder of the square is parts of the lower orders of 1 by those near it after the last lowest 5 is doubled plus 1 which is always added to it. Then the resulting root is 255 and 317 parts of 511 parts of 1.[27] If we multiply the remainder by 60 and we divide it by 511, it is in the falus of dirhams or minutes of degrees. That is what we wished to do.

Root of an Integer Plus Fractions

If we wish the root of an integer plus fractions, we convert the integer plus fractions to the category of the last fraction it has. Then when we see that the mark of the fraction is even, we extract its root. When the [mark of the] fraction is odd, we multiply it by 60 once again so that it is converted to a fraction with an even mark. Then its root is extracted, and if what remains of the square is zeros preceded by no number, take half of those zeros and put them before the resulting root.[28]

Section on the result if it is the root of degrees or the root of fractions with an even mark. Then the mark is half of the mark of that fraction. The root of seconds is minutes, the root of fourths is seconds, and so on by analogy.[29]

---

[27] For greater precision, ʿAnābī's Hebrew commentary (fol. 49a) gives the case where four zeros are added to a number to give two more places in the remainder.

[28] This is in the case of a perfect square.

[29] In the section on square root, the explanation in ʿAnābī's Hebrew commentary is very detailed and must have been indispensable for students since the Arabic text is generally very concise. Much of the Arabic text seems to be missing here. In ʿAnābī's Hebrew commentary (fol. 53a) a paragraph reads, "And when he says, 'And from the square root of the remaining fraction, take half before the fraction . . .,' he means that whatever you derived as the square root of the fraction, that is, aside from the square root of the integral part, then the fraction is half of that before the fraction whose square root is desired. This is as if there were eight ranks, then this would be four ranks." ואומרו ומשרש היתרון חצי לפני היתרון וכו׳ ירצה שמה שיצא לך ⟨ביתרון⟩ בשרש היתרון מזה ר״ל משרש הסחיח והיתרון הוא חצי לפני היתרון הנרצה השרש וזה שאם היתרון הוא ד״מ ח׳ מעלות זה יהיה ד׳ מעלות.
(The angle brackets enclose a word which is crossed out in the text.)
It would appear from this wording that something, whose half is taken, is before the fraction to indicate its power. The Hebrew terminology at this point is very weak so that the word for "degree" is used in the meaning of "rank" or "power." That it has the meaning of "mark" of the Arabic is quite certain. ʿAnābī does not seem to have been imaginative in his choice of technical terms. "That before the fraction" indicates its power of 60. "Half" refers to the exponent.

[FOLIO 273b]

٢٨٥

الصورة الخامسة ٣١٧ فالمراتب الفوقانية جذر المال

٥١١

والباقي من المال اجزاء من المراتب السفلانية من واحد المغرب

بعد ان نضاعف الخمسة الاخيرة من السفلانية ونحطها

واحدا بدا فالحاصل من الجذر اي خمسة وخمسون جزءا

والثمانية وسبعة عشر جزءا من خمسة مائة ولا من عشر اجزاء

من واحد فاذا ضربنا الباقي في ستين وثمانية يجي من ثلثة

واحد عشر حصل ثلوين من دراهم اوردناه في درج وذلك

ما اردنا ان نعمل جذر الصحاح والكسور فاذا

اردنا جذر صحاح وكسور نقلنا الصحاح والكسور الى

جنس الكسر الاخير الذي معه ثم نظرنا فان كان لفظ

الكسر زوج استخرجنا جذره وان كان فرد ضربناه في

ستين مرة اخرى لينتقل الى كسر لفظه زوج ثم نستخرج جذره

وان بقي من المال اصفار ليس قبلها عدد خذ نصف ذلك

الاصفار وتقدم على الجذر الحاصل فصل بان الحاصل من

فان كان جذر الدرج وكان جذر كسور لفظه زوج نصف لفظ

ذلك الكسر جذر الثواني دقائق وجذر الروابع ثواني وتقاس

عليه فصل التاسع في الموازين بميزان لكل المراتب

Ninth Section

On Arithmetic Checks[30]

The check is of all the separate place positions. It is that the single numerals are added and the nines are cast from it. What remains is the check of those place positions. For example, consider the place positions of the figure, 75,642. The single numerals are added to give 24. If nines are cast out, 6 remains which is the check of these place positions. If it is multiplied by the check of the multiplier and then the nines are cast out, it is equal to the resulting check of the multiplication.

When the check of the divisor is multiplied by the check of the result [of the division] and then the check of the remainder is added to it, and the nines are cast out, it is equal then to the check of the dividend.[31]

When the check of a square root is multiplied by itself and then the check of the remainder is added to it, the nines are cast out and it is equal to the check of the square.

These then are the principles which we need for the knowledge of most unknown quantities. I may say without qualification that they are sufficient for all astronomical calculations and business transactions among people of the world. But since the cube is not necessarily required in any of the astronomical procedures or business transactions, I have omitted it from this account, deferring its treatment until after the tables where I shall mention it by way of commentary.

We complete the first book with this section.[32] May God be praised for its exposition.

[30] Up to this point, the Hebrew and Arabic sections correspond. This ninth section corresponds with the Hebrew twelfth (fols. 54b-55a).

[31] The check here is not the same as that found in ʿAnābī's Hebrew commentary (fol. 54b): "The check of division is when you reckon the check of the quotient which is added to the check of the remainder and the nines are cast out; then this leftover is equal to the check arising from division."

[32] Cube root and results of cube root are not discussed in the Arabic until Section 6 of Book II; they are taken up here in ʿAnābī's Hebrew commentary (fol. 52a ff.) which otherwise has only the first book.

مفروضة وميزان جمع حروفها احادا والقي منها تسعة تسعة
فالباقي فهو ميزان تلك المراتب ومثاله مراتب صورتها
٦٢٤٢ نجمع حروفها احادا فيكون اربعة عشر فاذا
القي منها تسعة تسعة بقي منه ستة وهي ميزان المراتب
اذا ضرب في ميزان المضروب فيه والقي تسعة تسعة
كان مساويا لميزان المبلغ من الضرب وميزان المقسوم
عليه اذا ضرب في ميزان الخارج وزيد عليه ميزان الباقي
والقي تسعة كان مساويا لميزان المال المقسوم وميزان الجذر
اذا ضرب في نفسه وزيد عليه ميزان الباقي والقي تسعة
كان مساويا لميزان المجذور فهذه هي الاصول التي يحصر
البها معرفة اكثر المقادير المجهولة واحكام العمل بها كافية
في جميع الحساب النجومية والمعاملات التي تخرج من اهل
العالم فاما الكتب فلان الاحتياج اليه بين ... ذكر
في شيء من الاعمال النجومية والمعاملات اسقطته عن
هذه الجملة واخرته الى ما بعد الجداول لاورده هناك على
سبيل التعليق وختم المقالة الاولى بهذا الفصل
والحمد لله وحده

SECOND BOOK

ON COMPOUNDED MATTERS

COMPRISING SIXTEEN SECTIONS

For these three fundamentals which are multiplication, division, and [the extraction of] the root, there is another compound approach by way of a table known as the sexagesimal table. We wish to work with it in this book so that work with fractions be made easier and for a greater precision than that which preceded in simple matters; it does not cause difficulty. It consists only in the transfer of letters [representing numerals] from the tables to the dust board. It is necessary that one know first how to work with the table, the raising of numbers which are greater than 60, the placing of orders according to their positions, addition of a number to a number, and subtraction of a number from a number.

FIRST SECTION

On Description of the Table

These tables are composed for each of the numbers from 1 to 60. Every one of these is multiplied sixty times. A table is set down for it under that number in two rows. In the first row are the orders of 60 which there are of the multiple. In the second row are the parts of 60. The numbers which make up the tops of the tables are numbers of width [going across]. The tables[33] are called after them so that the numbers which make up the columns of the table are numbers of length

[33] Kūshyār ibn Labbān apparently lacked a word for "sub-table."

المقالة الثانية

في المركب تشتمل على ستة عشر فصلا

لهذه الاصول الثلثة التي هي الضرب والقسمة والتجذير
طريقة اخرى على مذهب الهند بجدول نعرفه جدول الستين
نريد ان نعمل بها في هذه المقالة لانها اذا عملت سهل
استعمال الكسور والاستقصاء في التدقيق بالاضافة الى العمل
من البسيط ولا يلزمنا كلفة غير نقل الحروف من الجداول التي
نعت والذي يجب ان نقدم على ذكر العمل به معرفة الجدول
ورفع الاعداد التي هي اكثر من ستين ووضع المراتب على منازلها
وزيادة عدد على عدد ونقصان عدد من عدد

الفصل الاول في صفة الجدول هذه الجداول
مركبة على ان نجد الاعداد التي من واحد الى ستين ووضع
كل واحد منها ستين مرة ووضع له جدول تحت ذلك العدد
في سطرين ففي السطر الاول مراتب الستين الكائنة
من المضعف وفي السطر الثاني اجزاء الستين فالاعداد
التي على رؤوس الجداول تسميها اعداد العرض والجداول
منسوبة اليها والاعداد التي في طول الجدول تسميها

so that each of the two [sets of] numbers is made distinct from the other when we mention them.

Example: We find in the table that apposite 25 of the numbers of width and 15 of the numbers of length, is 6 15. The 6[34] is multiples of 60 when we multiply 25 fifteen times; 15 is the excess and is parts of 60.

Second Section

On the Raising of Numbers

If a number we wish to use is greater than 60, then we raise it; we divide it and its successive quotients by 60, retaining the remainders and carrying on the division of quotients until a final quotient is obtained which does not contain a multiple of 60. Then we arrange the orders so that the [whole] parts of the result of the division are in the first of the place positions and the first remainder is in the last of the place positions. Then, under it, we put the fractions which are with the integral portions.

Example: We are given orders whose number is 15,621. We wish to raise it. We divide by 60; there results 260 and a remainder of 21. It is the first of the remainders; it is retained. Then we divide the 260 by 60 to give 4 and a remainder of 20. We set it all down with the quotient 4 of the second division, showing the remainder of the first division in third place, as in the figure.

04
20
21

If fractions were with this integer, then we would have put them under the 21. The first of these place positions is the 4 raised twice. The second is the 20 raised once. The third is the 21 degrees not raised. If there are fractions they follow it.

[34] Letter "waw" in the Arabic text.

أعداد الطول ليتميز احد العددين عن الآخر عند ذكرنا
له مثاله انا اخذنا في الجدول الذي تحته من أعداد
العرض وبازائه من اعداد الطول وبه فالواو
من السنين من تضعيفه خمسة عشر مرة وبقية الفاضل
هو اجزا من الستين الفصل الثاني في رفع الاعداد
اي عدد اردنا استعماله وكان اكثر من ستين رفعناه
اي قسمناه على الستين ما انقسم ونحفظ بالباقي
التي يبقى من القسمة وبالحاصل الذي يحصل في اجزاء
القسمة ثم نضع مراتبه على ان نجعل اجزاء الحاصل
من القسم اول المنازل واول الباقي اخر المنازل ثم نضع
تحته الكسور التي مع الصحاح مثاله عدد مراتب
عددها خمسة عشر الفا وستمائة واحد وعشرين نريد
ان نرفعه فنقسم على الستين يحصل مائتين وستين
احد عشرين وهو اول البواقي فنحفظه ثم نقسم المائتين
والستين على الستين يحصل الاربعة ويبقى عشرون
فنضع الجميع على ما في الاربعة الحاصلة ٤ ٢٠ ٢١ في
اجزا القسمة الثانية بانها الاول والثاني ولو كان

Third Section

On Addition

We wish to add 25 degrees 33 minutes and 24 seconds to 48 degrees 35 minutes and 15 seconds. We set it down according to what is in the first figure.

48	25	
35	33	[*Fig. 1*]
15	24	

The degrees are beside degrees, minutes beside minutes, and seconds beside seconds. Then we add the 25 to the 48, the tens to the tens, and the units to the units. Then we add the 33 to 35, and 24 to 15. Whenever it exceeds 60, we subtract 60 from it and add 1 to the place position above it.[35] This is the upper 1 as is shown in the second figure.

01		
14	25	
08	33	[*Fig. 2*]
39	24	

This is what we wished to do.

[35] A marginal addition in another hand gives this step.

مع هذه الصحاح كسورا وضعناها لتحفظ الاحاد

فالاول من هذه المنازل هي اربعة مرفوع من ثمانية والثانية

وهو العشرون مرفوع من الثالثة وهو الاحد والعشرين

درجات غير مرفوعة ويليها الكسور اذا كانت

الفصل الثالث في الزيادة نريد ان نزيد خمس وعشرين

درجة وثلثة وثلثين دقيقة واربعة وعشرين ثانية

على ثمانية واربعين درجة وخمسة وثلثين دقيقة

ثانية فنضعها على ما في الصورة الاولى ٢٥ ٣٣ ٢٤ | ٤٨ ٣٥ ١٥

الدرج بازاء الدرج والدقايق

بازاء الدقايق والثواني بازاء الثواني ثم نزيد الخمسة

والعشرين على الثمانية والاربعين العشرات على العشرات

والاحاد على الاحاد ونزيد الثلثة والثلثين على

الخمسة والثلثين والاربعة والعشرين على الخمسة عشر وكلما زادت

منزلة منها على ستين وزدنا على المنزلة التي قبلها واحدا

فيصير على ما في الصورة الثانية ٢٥ ٣٣ ٢٤ | [illegible] وذلك

ما اردنا ان نعمل والسلم

الفصل الرابع في النقصان نريد ان ننقص

Fourth Section

On Subtraction

We wish to subtract 25 degrees 33 minutes and 24 seconds from 48 degrees 35 minutes and 15 seconds. It is set down as is shown in the first figure.

48	25	
35	33	[*Fig. 1*]
15	24	

Each kind is beside its kind. Then we subtract 25 from 48, the tens from the tens, and the units from the units. Then we subtract the 33 from the 35, and the 24 from the 15. If we cannot subtract, we subtract a 1 from the place position before it and we add 60 to this place position. Then we subtract from that to which we added [the 60]. The result is shown in the second figure.[36]

23	25	
01	33	[*Fig.* 2]
51	24	

Subtraction by Another Method

We wish to halve 25 degrees 36 minutes and 23 seconds. We set it down according to the first figure.

25	
36	[*Fig. 1*]
23	

Then it is broken down. We halve the lowest 3, then its tens; then the 6, then its tens; then the 5, then its tens. And if in halving the units we get $\frac{1}{2}$, we add these [i.e. the 3 of the resulting 30] to the tens of the

[36] The Arabic has 34 in place of 24, presumably a scribal error.

خمسة وعشرين درجة وثلثة وثلثين دقيقة واربعة
وعشرين ثانية من ثمنية واربعين درجة وخمسة
وثلثين دقيقة وخمسة عشر ثانية فنضعها على ما في الصورة
الاولى كل جنس بازاء جنسه ثم ننقص
الخمسة والعشرين من الثمانية والاربعين العشرات
من العشرات والاحاد من الاحاد وننقص الثلثة
والثلثين من الخمسة والثلثين والاربعة والعشرين
من الخمسة عشر وما لم ينقص نقصنا من المنزلة التي
قبلها واحدا وزدنا له على هذه المنزلة ستين ثم نقصنا
منها ما نريد فحصل على ما في الصورة الثانية
ومن النقصان نوع اخر ونريد ان نضعف
خمسة عشر درجة وستة وثلثين دقيقة وثلثة
وعشرين ثانية فنضعه على ما في الصورة الاولى
ثم نبتدي فنضعف الثلثة السفلانية ثم عشراتها
ثم الستة ثم عشراتها ثم الخمسة ثم عشراتها فالاحاد
ان وقع في تضعيفها النصف زدنا على عشرات المنزلة
التي تليها من اسفل ثلثين والعشرات ان وقع في تضعيفها

place position which is next, lower. And if in halving the tens we get a 5, we add the 5 to its units. We thus obtain what is in the second figure.[37]

12	
48	
11	[*Fig. 2*]
30	

This is what we wished to do.

Fifth Section

On Multiplication

We wish to multiply 25 degrees 42 minutes by 18 degrees 36 minutes. We set it down according to the first figure.

18	25	
36	42	[*Fig. 1*]

The first place position of the multiplicand is that on the right of the calculator beside the first place position of the multiplier. The second is beside the second. Then a space is left between the two of them for the product.[38] We consult the table for 18, a number of the width, then take 25 apposite it which is of the numbers of the length. It gives 7 30. We put the 7 above and beside the 25. We put 30 beside the 25. If we do not find anything of the apposite one in the first line,[39] we put a 0 in place of the 7. Then we take the table again for what is apposite 42, which is 12 36. We add the 12 to what is above and beside the 42. We put the 36 beside the 42. We shift the multiplicand lower by a place to what is in the second figure.

	07		
18	42		
36	36	25	[*Fig. 2*]
		42	

[37] The fractional remainders of numbers which cannot be halved exactly must be shifted elsewhere. Half of the 3 of the 23 is $1\frac{1}{2}$. The $\frac{1}{2}$ is converted to the next lower order of sexagesimals as 30 thirds. There are no thirds to add it to so that 30 thirds remain. The 2 of the 23, when halved, becomes 1 so that we have 11 seconds. Then the 6 of the 36 becomes 3, and the 3 of the 36 becomes $1\frac{1}{2}$. The $\frac{1}{2}$, since it is in the tens, is multiplied by

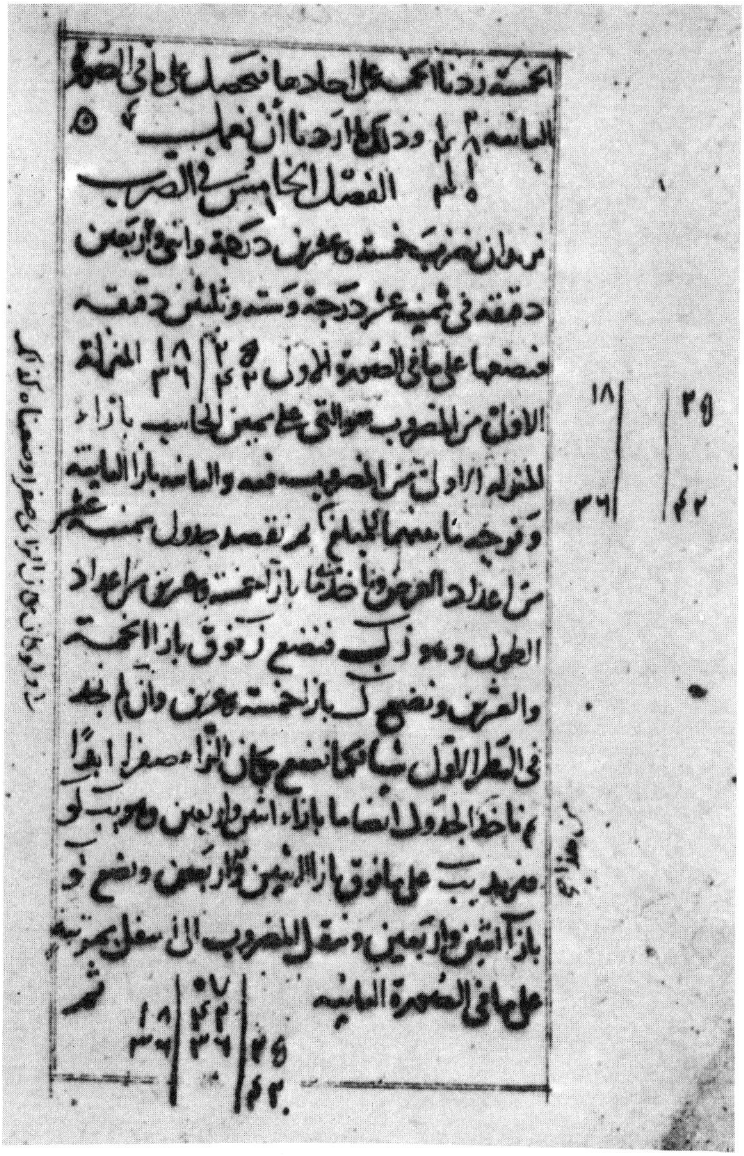

10 to bring it to 5 units of the minutes rank. This 5 is added to the 3 just obtained. This gives 18 for the minutes. When the 5 degrees of the 25 is halved it gives 2° 30′. The 30′ is added to the 18′ to give 48′. The 2 of the 25 is halved to give 1 so that 12° remains.

[38] In this section figures in the Arabic text are repeated in the margin, presumably for greater clarity.

[39] 7 30 would have appeared as $\frac{7}{30}$ in the table.

Then in the table for 36, which is taken as the number of width, we take what is apposite the 25 in the numbers of length. It is 15 0. We add the 15 to what is above and beside the 25, and the 0 to what is beside the 25. Then we take again from this table what is apposite the 42 to give 25 12. We add the 25 to what is above and beside the 42. The result of the multiplication is shown in the third figure.

	07		
18	58		
36	01	25	[*Fig. 3*]
	12	42	

Sixth Section

On the Result of Multiplication

By this is meant the first of the place positions of the answer.[40] We have set down a table for it following the sexagesimal table. Then we consider the number of the multiplicand in the length, and the multiplier in the width, then get the place of their meeting [in the table], and the result of the multiplication.[41]

Example: We wish the result of the multiplication of that raised once by that raised twice. We find 3 in black as their sum. We know that the first [part] of the result of it is raised three times, then what follows by its ordering until we reach the fractions, then the fractions by their ordering. The numerals in black signify the raised integers, and the numerals in red are the fractions. Let us know this.

[40] From this exponent, all the remaining orders become known.
[41] I.e. their powers of the 60 factor.

نقص جدولاً منه ويليه من اعداد العرض ونأخذ منه
بازاء خمسة وعشرين من اعداد الطول وهو يه ح
فنثبته على ما فوق بازاء الخمسة والعشرين والصفر لما
بازاء خمسة عشر ثم ناخذ من هذا الجدول ايضا بازاء
اثنين واربعين وهو كه يب فنثبتك على ما فوق
بازاء الاثنين والاربعين ونضع يب بازاء الاثنين والاربعين
فيحصل من الضرب على ما في الصورة الثالثة
وذلك ما اردنا ان نعمل
الفصل الثاني في نسخ الحاصل من الضرب
يعني به اول منازل المبلغ وقد وضعناه جدولا بعد
جدول الستين فاذا ما العدد المضروب طولا والمضروب
فيه عرضا فالتقاؤهما هو الحاصل من الضرب مثاله انا
اردنا الحاصل من ضرب المرفوع مرة واحدة في المرفوع مرتين
وجدنا عند ملتقاهما ثلثه بالسواد يعلمنا ان
اول الحاصل منه مرفوع ثلث مرات ثم ما يليه على ترتيبه
الى ان ينتهي الى المكسور ثم المكسورة على ترتيبها والحروف
بالسواد في الصحاح المرفوعة والحروف بالحمرة في

Seventh Section

On Division

We wish to divide 49 degrees 36 minutes by 12 degrees 25 minutes. We set down the two of them according to the first figure.

49	12
36	25

[*Fig. 1*]

The first place position of the dividend is beside the first of the divisor, the second beside the second.[42] Then we look [to see] in which table we find, apposite the 12 of the numbers of length then apposite 25 of it, that which equals the amount to be divided or what is close to it but less than it. Then we find in the table that the 3 of the numbers of width is in apposition to the 12 of the length to give 0 36. We set down the 3 which is of the numbers of the width to the left of the calculator. We subtract 36 from 49. Then we take what is apposite 25 of this table; it is 1 15.[43] We subtract 1 [from what is] above and beside the 25. We subtract 15 from what is beside the 25. Then we shift the divisor one place lower than it is, and it is according to what is in the second figure.

03	12	
	21	12
		25

[*Fig. 2*]

Then we look [to see] in which table we find, in apposition to the 12[44] of the numbers of the length, then in apposition to the 25 of it, that which is equal to the remainder of the amount to be divided or what

[42] The Arabic text here has "the second beside the third", presumably a scribal error.

[43] The table would show that the integer in the quotient of $49 \div 12$ is 4, but 4 is rejected because $4 \cdot 12°25' = 49°40'$ which is greater than the dividend, 49°36′. Still in the 3 table, $3 \cdot 25 = 75 = 1\ 15$.

[44] The Arabic text has 22 in place of 12, presumably a scribal error.

[FOLIO 277b]

approximates to it but is less than it. We find in the table that 59 of the numbers of the width, is in apposition to 12 with 11 48. We set down the 59 under the 3 placed first, and we subtract 11 from what is above and beside the 12 and the 48 from what is beside it. Then we take what is apposite the 25 of this table. It is 24 35. We subtract the 24 from what is above and beside the 25 and the 35 from what is beside it. It results according to what is in the third figure.[45]

03	00	
59	08	12
	25	25

[*Fig. 3*]

This is examined. Then, if we wish precision, we shift the divisor one more place lower. The result increases in precision. Where we finished, the result of division is 3 degrees and 59 minutes. There remains of the dividend that which is left in between two lines. And let us mention that where the first place position is not divisible by the divisor, then we set down a 0 in place of the result. We then shift the divisor without having changed it. This is what we wished to do.

Eighth Section

On the Result of Division

By the result of division is meant the [power of the] first of the place positions. We set down for it a table after the table of the multiplication.

[45] The figures in this section are repeated in the margins, and correct the mistakes in the text where fig. 2 does not have the divisor lowered and fig. 3 shows the 59 beside the 25.

المقسوم او ما يقاربه مما هو اقل منه فنجده في جدول
تسعة وخمسين من اعداد العرض ازاء اثني عشر بالخ
فنضع التسعة والخمسين تحت الثلثة الموضوعة اولا
وننقص ما بما فوق ازاء الاثني عشر ونجد ما بازائه
ثم ناخذ ما بازاء خمسة وعشرين من نفس الجدول وهو كذلك
ننقص كله مما فوق ازاء الخمسة والعشرين وله
ما بازائه فيحصل على هذه الصورة

٣	٥٩	٥٣
٢٥	٢٤	٤١

وهي هذه ثم ان اردنا التدقيق نقلنا
المقسوم عليه مرة اخرى الى اسفل زيد في النقل
زاد الحاصل دقيقة والى حيث انتهينا حصل من القسمة
ثلث درجات وتسعة وخمسين دقيقة وبقي من المقسوم
ما هو بان فيما بين الخطين والتذكر ان حيث ما لم
نقسم المنزلة الاولى من المقسوم عليه وضعنا ككل
الحاصل صفرا ونقلنا المقسوم عليه من غير عمل
وذلك ما اردنا ان نبين الفصل الثامن
في الحاصل من القسمة الحاصل من القسمة
يعني بها اولا نظار له وقد وضعنا له جدولا يتبعه جدول

	٥٥	٣
١٢	٥٨	٥٩
٢٥	[illegible]	٢

Then we consider the dividend in the width, and the divisor in the length; we determine the meeting place of the two of them to yield the result.

Example: We wish the result of division of seconds by fourths. We find at the place of meeting of the two of them a "2 times"[46] in black. Then we know that it is raised twice. The numerals in black are the raised integers while those in red are fractions. Let us know this.

Ninth Section

On Square Root

There are two types of square root. The first kind [includes] the root of raised degrees with fractions, or without fractions—the root is of raised degrees, the number of raisings of which is even, as one raised twice or four times, with or without fractions; and the root of fractions which have even marks like seconds, fourths, and sixths. The second kind [includes] the root of raised degrees but the number of times it is raised is odd, as once raised or thrice, with or without fractions; and the root of fractions which have odd marks, as thirds, minutes, and fifths.

As to the first kind we wish to extract the root of 45 degrees and 36 minutes. We set it down according to the first figure.

45
36

[*Fig. 1*]

[46] The Arabic text has the letter equivalent of "2" followed by two letters of a word which was apparently intended to be *marrāt*, "times," but which was left unfinished.

للضرب فيما للمقسوم عنه او المقسوم عليه طولا فلتقابلها
مع الحاصل مثاله انا اردنا الحاصل من قسمة الثواني
على الروابع فوجدنا عند ملتقاهما ف مر بالسواد
فعلمنا انه مرفوع مرتين والحروف بالسواد هي الصحاح
المرفوعة وبالحمرة هي الكسور فليعلم ذلك الفصل
التاسع في الجذر الجذر على وجهين فالوجه الاول منهما
جذر درجات مرفوعة بكسور او بغير كسور وجذر درجات
مرفوعة لكن عدد رفعها زوج كالمرفوع مرتين واربع مرات
بكسور او بغير كسور وجذر كسور لفظه زوج كالثواني
والروابع والسوادس والوجه الثاني جذر درجات
مرفوعة لكن عدد رفعها فرد كالمرفوعة مرة او ثلثة بكسور
او بغير كسور وجذر كسور لفظه فرد كالثوالث والدقائق
والخوامس اما الوجه الاول فبعيد ان نستخرج جذر خمسة
واربعين درجة وستة وثلثين دقيقة فنضعه على ما
في الصورة الاولى | ٤٥ / ٣٦ | ثم نطلب في جدول الضرب
جذرا يكون بازاء العدد المساوي له طولا خمسة واربعين
او ما هو اقرب اليه مما هو اقل منه وينبغي ان نجد ذلك

Then we search in the table for the same numbers of width and length which make 45 or what is close to but less than it. It is necessary that we find this type [of order] in the second row of the table—the first line of it is 0. We find the 6 table apposite another 6 of the numbers of the length gives 0 36. Then we set the 6 on the right and left of the calculator beside the 45. Then we subtract 36 from the 45. There remains 9. Then we double the right 6 and we shift it to the lower place on the right according to what is in the second figure.

6	09		
	36	12	[*Fig. 2*]

Then we examine the table to determine what is apposite the 12 to give 9 36 or what is closest to but less than it; after that there is a remainder. It will remain with the found number again. Then we find 45 in the table is apposite 12 as 9 0. Then we put 45 under the 12 on the right and under the 6 on the left. We subtract 9 from what is above and beside the 12. Then we take from this table what is apposite the 45 to give 33 45. We subtract 33 from what is above and beside the 45 and we subtract 45 from that beside it. There remains 2 15. Then we double the 45 on the right and we shift it from what its place is to a lower one according to this third figure.

06	00		
45	02		
	15	13	[*Fig. 3*]
		30	

Then we examine the table to find that apposite thirteen is 2 15 or what comes close to it but is less than it—when there is a remainder. It

في هذا الوضع في السطر الثاني من الجدول ويكون السطر
الاول منه صفراً نجد في جدول سته بازاء السته ايضاً من
أعداد الطول حج لو فنضع السته عن يمين الجانب وعن
يساره ايضاً بازاء خمسة واربعين وننقص لو من الخمسة
والاربعين فيبقى طه ثم نضاعف السته اليمنى في مكانها
٦ | ٥٩ | ٣٦ ٦
وننقلها الى اسفل بمنزلة على ما في الصورة الثانية
ثم ننظر في اي جدول نجد بازاء اثني عشر طو او ما يقرب
اليه مما هو اقل منه بحيث لان يكون الباقي يفي بالعدد الموجود
ايضاً نجد في جدول خمسة واربعين بازاء اثني عشر طحم
فنضع خمسة واربعين تحت الاثني عشر عن اليمين وتحت السته
عن اليسار وننقص طه مما فوق ازاء اثني عشر ثم نأخذ من هذا
الجدول ما بازاء الخمسة والاربعين وهو لحومه فننقص لح
مما فوق ازاء الخمسة والاربعين وننقص لو مما بازائه فيبقى
به ثم نضاعف الخمسة والاربعين اليمنى وننقلها مع ما
٦ | ٥٥ | ٥٢ | ١٥ | ١٣ ٣٥
٥٦ | ٥٥ | ٥٢ | ١
ننقلها بمنزلة الى اسفل على ما في الصورة الثالثة
ثم ننظر في اي جدول نجد بازاء اثني عشر ـه او ما
١٣ يقاربه مما هو اقل منه بحيث لان يكون الباقي يفي بالمراتب
٣٥

remains with the orders which are under the 13. Then we find 9 in the table apposite 13 is 1 57. We set down the 9 under the 30 on the right and under the 45 on the left. Then we subtract 1 from what is above and beside the 13, and 57 from what is beside it. Then we take from this table what is beside 30, 4 30. Then we subtract 4 from what is above and beside the 30 and 30 from what is beside it. Then we take from this table again what is apposite the 9; it is 1 21. We subtract 1 from what is above and beside the 9 and 21 from what is beside it. It then results according to what is in the fourth figure.

06	00	
45	00	
09	13	
	28	13
	39	30
		18

[*Fig. 4*]

If we double the 9 together with the place position preceding it one last time, and we work as we worked previously, then the result of the root is more exact, for the results on the left are the sought root. The remainder of the root is parts of the orders on the right, [which in turn are parts] of 1, after you double the 9 again and add 1 to it, [as] always.

Section on the second kind of root, there being no difference of procedure between it and the first in the work. It is necessary that we find the first sought after [number] in the first line of the table. There is or is not something with it in the second line. If we put the number which we put down first on the right and on the left beside the second place position of the roots, then that is what we wished to do.

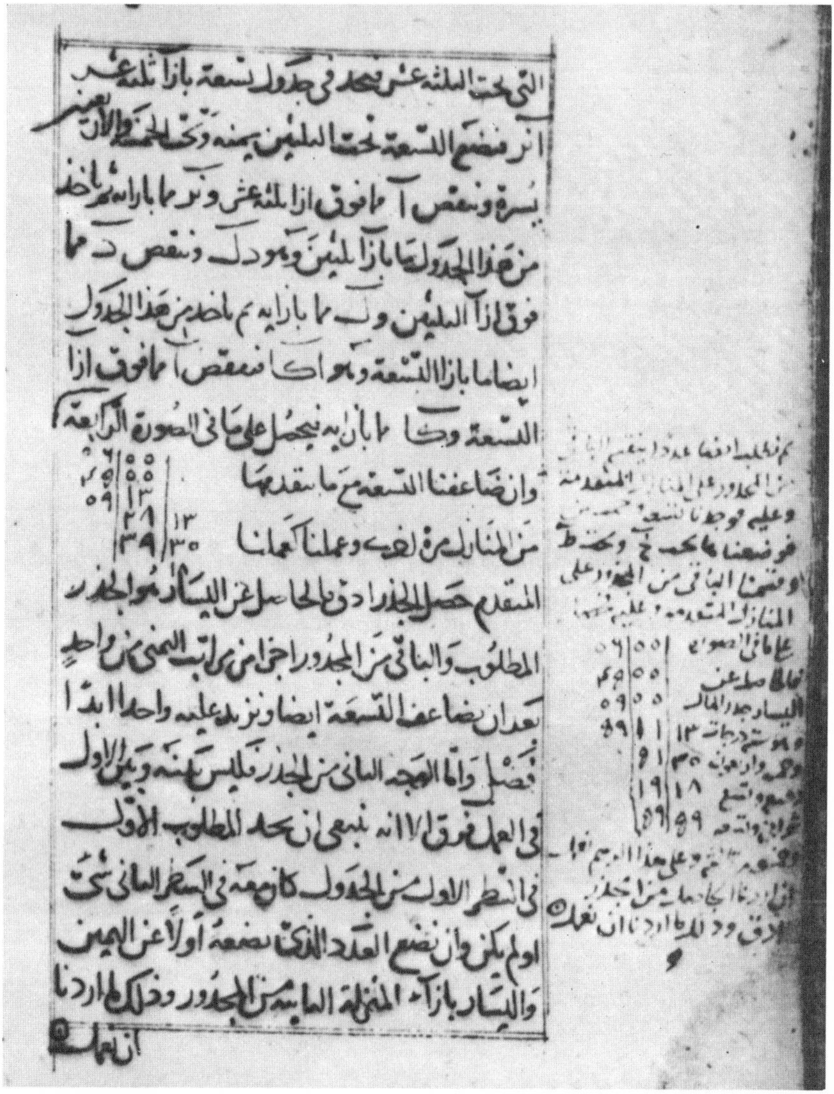

التي تحت الثلثة عشر نجد في جدول تسعة بازا ثلثة عشر
ان موضع التسعة تحت الثلثين يمنه وتحت الخمسة والاربعين
يسره وننقص آ مما فوق ازا الثلثة عشر ونرسم ما بازائه ثم ناخذ
من هذا الجدول لما بازا الثلثين وهو دل وننقص د مما
فوق ازا الثلثين و ل مما بازائه ثم ناخذ من هذا الجدول
ايضا ما بازا التسعة وهو اكا ننقص آ مما فوق ازا
التسعة وكا مما بازائه فيحصل على ما في الصورة الرابعة
وان ضاعفنا التسعة مع ما تقدمها
من المنازل مرة اخرى وعملنا كعملنا
المتقدم حصل الجذر دون الحاصل عن اليسار وهو الجذر
المطلوب والباقي من المجذور راجع من مراتب التي بين واحد
بعد ان ضاعف التسعة ايضا ونزيد عليه واحدا ابدا
فصل واما الوجه الثاني من الجذر فليس بينه وبين الاول
في العمل فرق الا انه ينبغي ان نجد المطلوب الاول
في السطر الاول من الجدول كان وضعه في السطر الثاني تحت
اوله لكن وان نضع العدد الذي نضعه اولا عن اليمين
واليسار بازاء المنزلة الرابعة من المجذور وذلك لما اردنا
ان نعلم

Tenth Section

On the Results of Square Root

The results of square root are according to four kinds: (1) the root raised more than once, (2) the root raised one time or not raised, (3) the root of fractions whose mark is odd, (4) the root of fractions whose mark is even.

Section on the root of the [number] raised more than once. We halve the exponent belonging to the amount whose root was taken. If a fractional exponent occurs in it indicating a fractional remainder, then it is a number whose exponent is one less in the resulting place position; then that which is raised four times has a root raised twice. That raised seven times has a root raised three times.

Section on the root [of a number] raised one time or not raised. It is in degrees not raised.

Section on the root of fractions having even marks. We halve whatever the mark of the number is. It is the root, as the root of seconds is minutes, and the root of fourths is seconds.

Section on the root of fractions having odd marks. We add 1 to it, then we halve it. The root of fifths is thirds; the root of sevenths is fourths. In this section, we make the root larger than that whose root is taken. Let this be known.

Eleventh Section

On Checks

The check of any given place positions is that all their digits are added and the nines cast out from them. The remainder is multiplied by 6 and added to the digits of the second place position. The nines are cast

الفصل العاشر في الحاصل من الجذر

الحاصل من الجذر على اربعة اوجه أ جذر المرفوع الكثير من مرة
ب وجذر المرفوع مرة او غير مرفوع ج وجذر كسور د
لفظه فرد د وجذر كسور لفظه زوج فصل فجذر المرفوع
الكثير من مرة بنصف عدد رفع الجذور فان وقع فيه كسر
القيناه الكسر وما بقي فهو عدد رفع اول المنازل الحاصل
فالمرفوع اربع مرات جذره مرفوع مرتين والمرفوع سبع
مرات جذره مرفوع ثلث مرات فصل وجذر المرفوع مرة
او غير مرفوع درجات غير مرفوعة فصل وجذر كسور
لفظه زوج بنصف عدد لفظها ثان فمع الجذر جذر الثوا
دقايق وجذر الروابع ثواني فصل وجذر كسور لفظه فرد
نزيد عليه واحد ثم ننقصه فجذر الخوامس ثوالث وجذر
السوابع روابع وفي هذا الفصل نزيد الجذر على الجذور فليعلم

الفصل الحادي عشر في الموازين

ميزان جمل
منازل مفروضة هو ان نجمع حروفها اولها احادا ونلقي
منها تسعة تسعة ونصب الباقي في سطر ونضاف الى الحروف
المنزلة الثانية ونلقي منها تسعة تسعة ونصب الباقي

out of this one and the remainder multiplied by 6. The digits of the third place position are added to it. The nines are cast out from it. Then the remainder is the check of the three place positions.

Example: The place positions are as in this figure.

25
38
46

We add the 5 and the 2 to get 7, then multiply it by 6 to get 42. We add 8 and 3 to it to get 53. Nines are cast out from it to get 8. We multiply by 6 to get 48 and add 6 and 4. This gives 58. Nines are cast out from it; 4 remains. It is the check of these place positions.

Section: If the check of the multiplicand is multiplied by the check of the multiplier, and nines are cast out, then the check of the product equals the check of the result of multiplication [of check by check].

Section: If the check of the divisor is multiplied by the check of the quotient, and the check of the remainder is added to it, then nines are cast out, it equals the check of the dividend.

Section: The check of the root is if it is multiplied by itself and the check of the remainder is added to it, and nines are cast out, then it is equal to the check of the square of the root. Let us know this.

Twelfth Section

On the Results Following That Which Preceded

If an integral number is raised and we wish to know how many times it is raised, we count the place positions and subtract 1. For example, for

تسعة

في ستة ونضاف الى الحاصل في المنزلة الثالثة ويلقى منها تسعة

فيكون الباقي ميزان المنازل الثلثة مثاله منازل

هكذا ٤ ٩ ٢ ٣ ٢ ٩ فنجمع الخمسة والاثنين فيكون سبعة

فنضربه في ستة فيكون اثنين واربعين ونضيف اليه الثمنيه

والثلثة فيكون ثلثة وخمسين فيلقى منها تسعة تسعة فيبقى

ثمنية فنضربه في ستة تكون ثمانية واربعين فنضيف اليه

الستة والاربعة فتكون ثمنية وخمسين فيلقى منها تسعة تسعة

فيبقى اربعة وهو ميزان عدة المنازل فصل وميزان المضروب

اذا ضرب في ميزان المضروب فيه والقى تسعة تسعة كان

الباقي مثل ميزان المبلغ فصل وميزان المقسوم عليه اذا

ضرب في ميزان الخارج وزيد عليه ميزان الباقي والقى

تسعة تسعة كان مثل ميزان المقسوم فصل وميزان

الجذر اذا ضرب في نفسه وزيد عليه ميزان الباقي والقى

تسعة تسعة كان مثل ميزان المال المجذور فليعلم ذلك

الفصل الثاني عشر في [illegible] كما تقدم

اذا كان عدد صحاح مرفوع واردنا ان نعلم كم مرتبة رفع

تعدد المنازل ونقص منه واحد كلك منازل من العدد

المراتب فاكان ينقص منه واحدا ابدا

فابقي فهو عدد رفعه ٥

فنقول ميزان منازل العمود هكذا
ناخذ الخمسة والاثنين ٧ ٤ ٢
فيكون سبعة وهو ٨ ٣ ٢
ميزان المنزلة ٥ ٥ ٥
الاولى فنضعه بازائه ١ ٢ ٦
ثم نضربه في ستة ونزيد عليه الثمنية والثلثة
ونلقي ما اجتمع تسعة تسعة فيبقى ثمنية
وهو ميزان المنزلتين فنضعه بازائه
ثم نضربه في ستة ولا نزيد عليه شيئا
لان المنزلة الثالثة صفر ونلقي منها
تسعة تسعة فيبقى [illegible] وهو ميزان
الثلث منازل فنضعه بازائه ثم
نضربه في ستة ونزيد عليه الستة
والاربعة ونلقي ما اجتمع تسعة تسعة
فيبقى واحدا وهو ميزان المنازل
الاربعة فنضعه بازائه وعلى هذا
الرسم ٥

three place positions of the integral number, the integer is raised twice, and for four place positions, it is raised three times.[47]

Section: Again, if we divide a raised [number] by a raised one and we wish to know from the division how many place positions of the result there are as far as degrees not raised, we subtract the number of raisings of the divisor from the number of raisings of the dividend. To what remains, we always add 1. This is the number of the place positions of the result of the division as far as degrees not raised.

Example: The dividend is raised eleven times and the divisor six times. Between them there is 5. We add 1 to it; then the place position of the sixth in the result of division is degrees not raised. This is necessary for the reckoning.

Section: When we divide an amount by an amount and there remains a place position of the dividend, and we wish to distinguish its category, we examine how many place positions were taken from the dividend. What remains is the category of the remainder.

Example: The first of the place positions of the dividend is degrees. Three is subtracted from the place positions to give the first of the place positions of the remainder as thirds. Let this be known.

Thirteenth Section

On the Sexagesimal Table[48] and Its Consequences

The tables of the result of multiplication. Then there are the tables of the result of division. Then the sixteenth section is on the simple [i.e. in the decimal system] cube root.

---

[47] For example, a three place integral number as 5 4 3 ($5 \cdot 60^2 + 4 \cdot 60^1 + 3 \cdot 60^0$) is raised twice, or the difference in exponents is 2 minus 0 equal to 2.

[48] The tables are missing as are also sections 14 and 15 which probably showed the use of the tables in multiplication and division respectively.

الصحاح مرفوع مرتين الاربع منازل مرفوع لست مرات
فصل وايضا اذا قسمنا مرفوعا على مرفوع واردنا ان
نعلم كم منازل الحاصل من القسمة يكون درجا غير مرفوع
نقصنا عدد رفع المقسوم عليه من عدد رفع المقسوم
فما بقي نزيد عليه واحدا ابدا فما كان فهو عدد منازل
الحاصل من المقسوم حتى يكون درجا غير مرفوع ٥
مثاله ان المقسوم مرفوع احدى عشرة مرة والمقسوم
عليه ست مرات فبينهما خمسة فنزيد عليها واحدا فالمنزلة
السادسة من الحاصل من القسمة درج غير مرفوع وهذا
خلاف ما في العدد فصل واذا قسمنا عددا على عدد
وبقي من المقسوم منازل نريد ان نفرق جملته نظرنا
كم منزلة نقص من المقسوم فما بقي فهو جنس الباقي
مثاله اول منازل المقسوم درج ونقص من
منازله ثلثة فيكون اول منازل الباقي ثوالث
الفصل الثالث عشر في جدول الستين وتلوه
جدول الحاصل من الضرب ثم جداول الحاصل من
القسمة ثم الفصل السادس عشر في الكعب البسيط ٥

Sixteenth Section

On Extraction of Cube Root[49]

This chapter is informative regarding four rows, first the row of the extracted cube root called the uppermost row. Then under it is the row of the amount. Under the amount is a row of zeros. We call it the middle row. Under the middle row is what we call the lowest. We set down the amount and count it off in periods [from the right]. The period is marked off until we come to the last one. A number is set down under it in the lowest row, and above it and beside it in the uppermost row. We multiply it by itself and add the answer to the middle. Then we multiply the uppermost by the middle and cast it away from the amount. Then we double the number in its lowest place. We multiply the uppermost by the orders of the lowest and add the answer to the middle. Then we add the uppermost to the lowest and we shift the middle one place and the lowest by two places. Then we seek another number according to the preceding method and rules, and we do the same with it.

Example: We wish a cube root. The amount is this[50] number. We set it down on the dust board and we count off and mark the periods [of three digits each] until we reach the last, occupied by the 2. Then we set down under it a row of zeros;

2986100
0000000 [*Fig. 1*]

and under this and above the row of the amount is 1. We multiply the uppermost by the lowest and we add the answer to the middle. Then we multiply the uppermost by the middle and we cast it off from the amount. Then we have this:

1
1986100
1000000 [*Fig. 2*]
1

[49] This section corresponds with chapter ten of ʿAnābī's Hebrew text (fol. 52a).
[50] In the Arabic text, a red line goes from "this" to the number 2986100.

[FOLIO 281b]

الفصل السادس عشر في الكعب نقسم هنا الباب
أربعة أسطر الأول سطر الكعب الخارج ونسميه السطر
الأعلى وتحته سطر المال وتحت المال سطر الأصفار نسميه السطر الأوسط
نضع المال ونعده بمنطق واصمين منطق واصمين إلى أن
ننتهي إلى المنطق الأخير نضع تحته في السطر الأسفل
وفوقه بإزائه في السطر الأعلى عددا نضربه في نفسه ونزيد
المبلغ على الأوسط ونضرب الأعلى في الأوسط ونلقيه
من المال مضاف العدد في مكانه الأسفل
ونضرب الأعلى في مراتب الأسفل ونزيد المبلغ على الأوسط
ونزيد الأعلى على الأسفل وننقل الأوسط بمرتبة والأسفل
بمرتبتين ثم نطلب عددا آخر على الرسم المتقدم وشرائطه
ونعمل به العمل الأول سوا مثاله نريد كعب مال
عدده هذا نضعه على نحو نعلمه بمنطق واصمين فيقع
٢ ٩ ١ ٦ ٦ ١ ٥ ٥
المنطق الأخير تحت الاثنين فنضع
٥ ٥ ٥ ٥ ٥ ٥ ٥ ٥
بإزائه تحت سطر الأصفار وبإزائه فوق سطر المال
واحدا ونضرب الأعلى في الأسفل ونزيد المبلغ على الأوسط
ونضرب الأعلى في الأوسط ونلقيه من المال فيبقى هذا

We double the lowest in its place and then we multiply the uppermost by the lowest and we add the answer to the middle. Then we add the uppermost to the lowest and shift the middle one place and the lowest two places. Then it is according to the third figure.

```
1
1986100
 300000        [Fig. 3]
   3
```

Then we seek a number which is multiplied by the 3 of the middle, and the uppermost is multiplied by the lowest and cast off from the quantity.[51] We find it is 4.[52] We set it down beside the lowest 3 and above the 6 of the amount. Then we multiply the uppermost by the orders of the lowest and we add the answer to the middle. Then we multiply the uppermost by the middle and subtract it from the amount. There remains that which is according to the fourth figure.

```
1   4
 242100
 436           [Fig. 4]
   34
```

Then we double the lowest 4 and multiply the uppermost by the orders of the lowest and add the result to the middle. Then we add the uppermost to the lowest, and we shift the middle one place and the lowest two places. What results is according to the fifth figure.

```
1   4
 242100
   58800       [Fig. 5]
      42
```

Then we seek another number according to the preceding method. We find that it is 4. We set it down beside the lowest 2 and above it[self]

[51] The statement in the Arabic text for the required operation is wrong. To avoid confusion the statement should be corrected as follows: Then we seek a (maximum) number such that when its product by the order of the 3 of the lowest is added to the order of the middle, then the product of the uppermost by the middle is less than the corresponding amount.

[52] The 4 is repeated in the Arabic text, presumably a scribal error.

١

١٩٨٦١٠٠ ثم نضاعف الاسفل بمكانه ونضرب
١٠٠٠٠٠٠

الاعلى في الاسفل او نزيد المبلغ على الاوسط ونزيده على

على الاسفل وننقل الاوسط بمرتبة والاسفل بمرتبتين

فيكون على ما في الصورة الثالثة ١٩٨٦١٠٠ ثم نطلب
٣٠٠٠٠٠

٣

عددا نضربه في المثلثة للاوسط ونضربه للاعلى في

الاسفل ونلقيه من المال فنجده اربعة ارجعه فنضعه

بجنب المثلثة السفلية وبازايه فوق الستة من المال

ثم نضرب الاعلى في مراتب الاسفل ونزيد المبلغ على

الاوسط ونضرب الاعلى في الاوسط ونلقيه من المال

٣ ١

فيبقى على ما في الصورة الرابعة ٢٢٣٢١٠٠
٢٣٦٠٠٠

ثم نضاعف الاربعة السفلية ٢٣
٣٢

ونضرب الاربعة العلوية في مراتب الاسفل ونزيد

المبلغ على الاوسط ونزيد الاربعة العلوية على الاسفل

وننقل الاوسط بمرتبة والاسفل بمرتبتين فيكون على

٣ ١

ما في الصورة الخامسة ٢٢٣٢١٠٠ ثم نطلب
٤٨٨٥٠

عددا آخر على الرسم المتقدم ٣٢ فنجده اربعة

ونضعه جنب الاربعة السفلى وفوقه في السطر الاعلى

in the uppermost row. Then we multiply the uppermost by the orders of the lowest, and then we add the answer to the middle. We multiply the uppermost by the middle and then subtract it from the amount. There remains that which is according to the sixth figure.

1 4 4	
116	
60496	[*Fig. 6*]
424	

Then we double the lowest 4 and we multiply the uppermost by the orders of the lowest. We add the answer to the middle. We always add 1 to what falls out in the middle with the completion of the work. Then it is according to the seventh figure.

1 4 4	
116	
62209	[*Fig. 7*]
428	

The result[53] is in the uppermost line as the cube root of the amount. The remainder of the amount is parts of the orders of the middle, of 1. Whoever would make the cube root more exact must convert the amount to fractions to determine the cube root; these are thirds, sixths, and ninths according to this arrangement. Then its cube root is extracted.

As to the check of the cube root, if one multiplies it by itself, then by the check, and we add the check of the remainder of the amount whose cube root was extracted, and then nines are cast out, it is equal to the check of the amount whose cube root was derived.[54]

These are the principles existing in all of practical and astronomical arithmetic that flows from people of the world. It is concluded with the parts of this section. Praise be to God and may He have mercy on Muhammad to the last.[55]

---

[53] In ʻAnābī's Hebrew commentary (fol. 54b), there is a short chapter (ch. 11) on results of extracting cube root which reads: "The result of the cube root of degrees is degrees. The result of the cube root of thirds is minutes, and of the cube root of sixths is seconds, and of the cube root of ninths is thirds. Always do so in this fashion." השער הי״א בעולה מהקעב העולה מקעב מעלות הוא מעלות· ומקעב השלישים דקים ומקעב הששים שניים ומקעב התשעים שלישי׳ ועל זה הנוסח עשה לעולם·

[54] For example, in the problem of the text: $144 = 0 \pmod 9$. Check of the remainder $116 = 8$; $0 + 8 =$ check of the [2986100] $= 8$; and $8 = 8$.

[55] The final sentence of the Hebrew commentary reads: "Thus is completed the Hindu arithmetic of ibn Ḥasān Gûšiyyār which the accomplished sage, our master and teacher, R. Shālôm B. Kh. R. Joseph ʻAnābī, translated from Arabic into Hebrew together with a commentary by the aforementioned scholar and translator. Praise the Foremost who

[FOLIO 282b]

gave us the power and encouraged us.” נשלם חשבון ההנדיים לאבן חצאן גאושייר אשר
העתיקו מרנ׳ ורבנ׳ החכם השלם ר׳ שלום בכ״ר יוסף ענבי מלשון ערבי ללשון עברי ‹והשבי׳›
עם ביאור החכם המעתיק הנזכר· והשבח לראשון שזיכנו ושעורנו עד הנה כית . . .

(The angle brackets enclose a word which is crossed out in the text.)

GLOSSARY

units	احاد
difference	اختلاف
to extract [the root]	استخرج
aṣamm—see page 11 of the Introduction	اصّم
numbers of length	اعداد الطول
numbers of width, numbers going across	اعداد العرض
[order of] thousands	الوف
[order of] thousand thousands	الوف الوف
apposite, or meeting in the body of a table	بازاء
remainder	باقى
to expand, to spread out	بسط
ordering [of sexagesimals]	ترتيب
dust surface, dust board	تخت
doubling	تضعيف
halving	تنصيف
thirds	ثوالث
seconds	ثوانى
sexagesimal table	جدوا الستين
root, square root	جذر
rank, power of an exponent	جلس

to add	جمع
quotient, result of division	حصل من القسمة
result	حاصل pl. حواصل
numeral	حرف pl. حروف
fifths	خوامس
degree	درج
dirham	درهم
minutes	دقايق
place order	رتبة
to raise [the power of a number] by division by sixty	رفع
fourths	روابع
even	زوج
addition	زيادة
row	سطر
"lower number," multiplier	سفلانية
sevenths	سوابع
sixths	سوادس
raised integer	صحاح مرفوعة
zero	صفر pl. اصفر
symbol of the numerals	صور الحروف
to make multiples of, to multiply	ضاعف
to square	ضرب في نفسة
to double	ضعف
number	عدد
[order of] tens	عشرات
[order of] ten thousands	عشرات الوف
[order of] ten thousand thousands	عشرات الوف الوف

Glossary

astronomy	عمال النجومية
odd	فرد
fals	فلس
"the upper," multiplicand	فوقانية
division	قسمة
fraction	كسر
cube, cube root	كعب
mark, expression	لفظ
even mark	لفظ زوج
odd mark	لفظ فرد
to cast out [as nines], to cast off, to subtract	لقى
square, amount	مال
[order of] hundreds	مائين
[order of] hundred thousands	مأيين الوف
[order of] hundred thousand thousands	مأيين الوف الوف
product	مبلغ
raised [as when an exponent is increased]	مرفوع
raised four times	مرفوع اربع مرات
raised twice	مرفوع مرتين
multiplication	مضرب
multiplicand	مضروب
multiplier	مضروب فية
dividend	مقسوم
divisor	مقسوم عليه منازل
place positions	منازل
munṭaq—see page 11 of the Introduction	منطق
proofs	مولدان

indicator, check [in casting out of nines]	میزان موازین .pl
to halve	نصف
subtraction	نقصان
to convert [powers], to shift [orders]	نقل

INDEX

Abgad (*or* abjad) numeration: table of Greek, Hebrew, and Arabic, 8
Abū al-Fadāʿ: influence of Kūshyār on, 4
Abu Ḥanīfa, 41
Abū Kāmil: influence of, 3; algebra of, 3
Abū Sahl ibn Tamim: use of ghubār numerals by, 6
Abū al-Wafāʾ: book on arithmetic by, 3
Addition: Arabic name for, 9; of decimals using the dust board, 12; of sexagesimals using the dust board, 13–14; Kūshyār's decimal operations in, 48; Kūshyār's sexagesimal procedure in, 76
Alexandri de Villa Dei: fundamental operations of, 35
Algorism: Hebrew and Arabic versions of Kūshyār's, 5; etymology of the term, 34
Algorisms: Arabic, 3
ʿAnābī, Shālôm ben Joseph: life of, 4–5; translation by, 5, 8, 9, 49–56, 58–60, 62, 64, 68, 70, 100, 104
Approximation of the remainder in cube root: by Kūshyār, al-Nasawī, Leonardo, and Heron, 30–32
Approximative method in square root: by al-Nasawī, al-Ḥaṣṣār, and al-Qalaṣādī, 22–23
Arabic science: apogee of, 3
Arithmetic: Kūshyār's principles of, 34; purpose of, 44; four principles of, 44; Hindu, 45
Arithmetic mean: approximation of the second order by excess, 22
Āryabhaṭa: place value notation in, 6

al-Baihaqī, 40
Bakhshālī manuscript: place value notation in the, 6
Benedict, S. R., 34, 36
Ben Gerson, Levi: use of separator symbol by, 8; complete sexagesimal calculation unknown by, 19; fundamental operations of, 35
Bhāskara I: place value notation in, 6
al-Bīrūnī: lack of a pure sexagesimal operation in, 19
Boncompagni, B., 23, 41
Boyer, C. B., 34
Brahmagupta: place value notation in, 6
Brockelmann, C., 4

Cantor, M. B., 23, 31, 36, 41
Cardanus: addition of three zeros to obtain a more exact cube root by, 32
Chace, A. B., 36
Checks: errors in, 33; arithmetic, 70; mod 9 method of, 94–96
Chuquet, N., 23, 40
Coinage: sexagesimal, 37
Comtino, M.: use of a separator symbol by, 8
Conversion of integers to sexagesimals in division, 18
Cube root: Arabic term for, 10; al-Nasawī's operation of, 25; Kūshyār's operation of, by decimals, 26–28, 100–104

Decimals: Indian, 6; need for order indicatiors in, 7; multiplication of, 14; conversion by tables to sexagesimals, 38
De la Roche, Estiénne: approximative method by interpolated fractions, 23
Denominatio, 36
Denomination: definition of, 36; use of tables in, 38
Diophantus: translator of, 3
Division: Arabic name for, 9; decimal operation of, 15; mixed numbers in, 16–18; exponential rules in, 18; decimal

procedure of Kūshyār in, 58 ff.; power of the result in, 62, 86; sexagesimal procedure of Kūshyār in, 84–86
Divisor: Arabic name for, 9
Doubling: fundamental operation, 35–36; not considered by Fibonacci and ibn Ezra, 36; transmission of, 36; decimal operation of, 49
Duhem, P., 25
Dust board: construction, 5; erasing figures on, 5–6; use by al-Ḥaṣṣār, 23; use of, 41

Enesröm, G., 25, 34, 41
Euclid: translator of, 3
Exponents: mathematical terminology for, 9; term of al-Qalaṣādī for, 10; terms of al-Kāshī, 10; rules for, 18; Kūshyār's notion of, 39; al-Khwārizmī's, 40

Fihrist, 6
Flügel, G., 4, 6
Fourths: Arabic term for, 10
Fractions: in sexagesimal calculation, 6; Arabic term for, 11

Gemma Frisius: approximation in the result of the cube root by, 32

Halliwell[-Phillipps], J. O., 34
Halving: Arabic name for, 9; Judaeo-Arabic term for, 11; operation of, 12; sexagesimal, 14; as a fundamental operation, 35–36; transmission of, 36; not considered by Leonardo Fibonacci and ibn Ezra, 36; decimal procedure of Kūshyār in, 50–52; sexagesimal procedure, 78
Hammer-Purgstall, J., 6
Harmonic mean: approximation of the second order by defect by the, 22
al-Ḥaṣṣār: numerals of, 7; use of approximative method by, 23; al-Nasawī compared as a mathematician with, 25
Heath, T. L., 31
Heiberg, J., 38
Heron: approximation in the result of the cube root by, 31
Hindu arithmetic, 45
Hindu numerals, 3, 6
Ḥisāb al-ghubār, 6
Hochheim, A., 6, 23, 24
Hundreds: Arabic term for, 9

Ibn al-Bannā': numerals of, 6; comments of al-Qalaṣādī on, 23
Ibn Ezra, Abraham ben Meir: use of symbol to separate integers from fractions by, 8; fundamental operations of, 35
Ibn Labbān. *See* Kūshyār ibn Laban
Ibn al-Majdī, 41
Ibn Tibbon, Moses, 23
Ibn al-Waḥshīya: Hindu numerals as an alphabet in, 6
Indicator: use in checking operation of mod 9, 10; general use, 32
Integer: in sexagesimal calculation, 6; sexagesimal Judaeo-Arabic term for, 11
ʿIyyūn hāʿiqqārīm, 4

al-Jāḥiẓ: Hindu numerals of, 6
John of Seville: lack of a pure sexagesimal operation in, 19
Jordanus Nemorarius: fundamental operations of, 35; dependence upon al-Nasawī, 41

Kāfī fī al-ḥisāb, 3
al-Karajī: algorism of, 3; numerals, 6, 25; sexagesimal reckoning of, 19; fundamental operations of, 35
Karpinski, L. C., 35
al-Kāshī: algorism of, 4; mathematical terminology of, 9; sexagesimal addition of, 14; sexagesimal operations of, 19; mod 59 check in sexagesimals by, 33; errors in checks, 33; sexagisimal tables of, 38; idea of exponents in, 40
Kennedy, E. S., 4, 37
al-Khwārizmī: algebra, 3; conversion of integers to lowest sexagesimals, 18; lack of a pure sexagesimal operation in, 19; term algorism from, 33; fundamental operations of, 34
Krause, M., 4
Kūshyār ibu Labbān: works of, 4; astrolabe, astronomy, and geography, 4; life, 4; algorismic texts in Hebrew and Arabic, 5; innovator in mathematical terminology, 9; influence of arithmetic of, 14, 40; approximative method in square root, 22–23; fundamental operations of, 34; denomination as an operation in, 36

Lalla: place value in the notation of, 6
Lambo, Ch., 23
Lange, G., 19
Lelewel, J., 4
Leonardo Fibonacci: effect of abū Kāmil's work on, 3; approximation of cube root by, 31; errors in checks by, 33; fundamental operations of, 35
Levey, Martin: work on abū Kāmil's algebra, 3; on Kūshyār's indeterminate equations, 34, 41
Luckey, P., 19, 40